Saints of Sind

Saints of Sind

PETER MAYNE

London

First published by John Murray in 1956
This new edition published by Eland Publishing Ltd
61 Exmouth Market, London EC1R 4QL in 2026

Copyright © Peter Mayne 1956

The right of Peter Mayne to be identified as author of this work has been asserted in accordance with the Copyright, Designs and Patents Act 1988

ISBN 978 1 78060 240 0

All rights reserved. This publication may not be reproduced, stored in a retrieval system or transmitted in any form or by any means, electronic, mechanical, photocopying, recording, or otherwise, without permission in writing from the publishers.

A full CIP record for this book is available from the British Library

Cover image: *At the Shrine of Lal Shahbaz Qalandar, Pakistan 2006*
© Reza/Getty Images Reportage

Text set in Great Britain by James Morris

For
W. A. L. B.

Contents

1	*Mister Peacock*	9
2	*A Cushion in the Skies*	31
3	*Rock-a-Bye Baby*	79
4	*Pagāro – I*	99
5	*Pagāro – II*	127
6	*A Frieze of Dervishes*	149
7	*The World is a…*	185
	About the Author	201

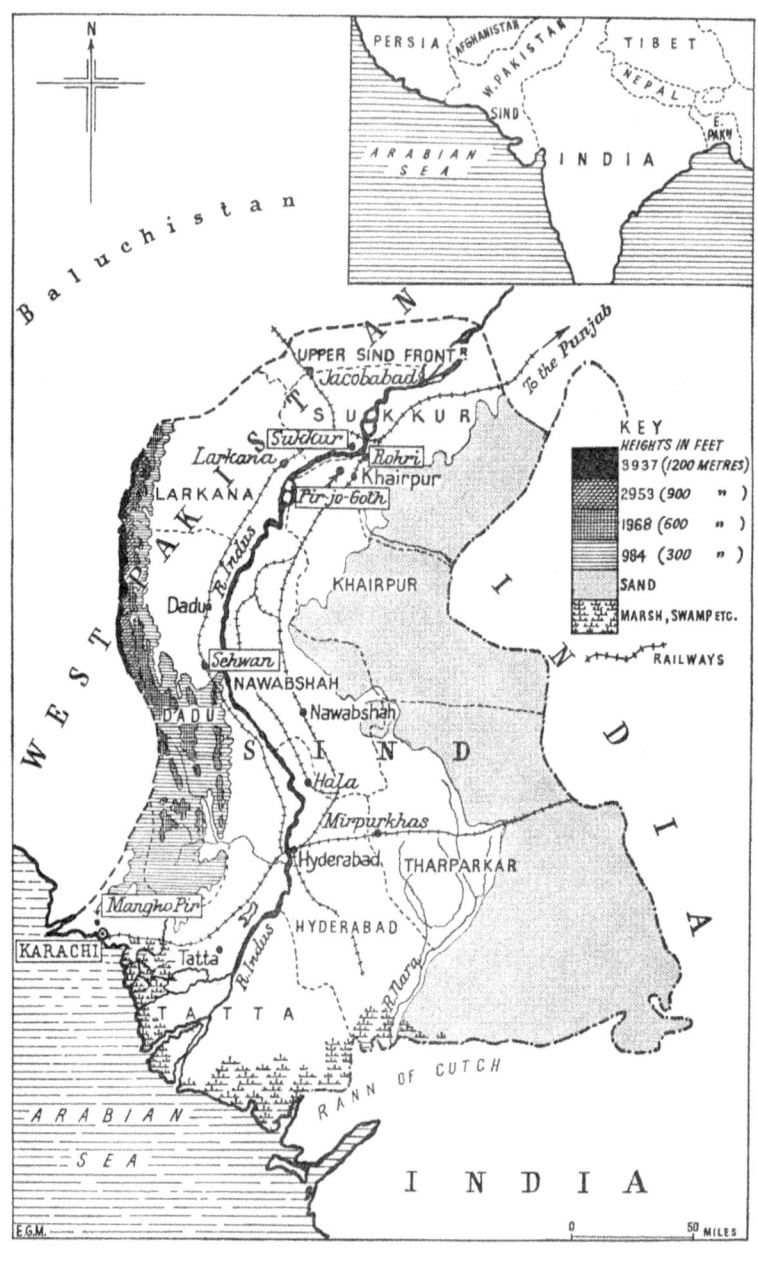

1
Mister Peacock

MISTER PEACOCK lives some ten miles north of Karachi, in the foothills. It is arid, unrelenting country, but he has the best of it. He lives in an oasis, with a pool of dark water surrounded by rocks and palm-trees, and at the particular point where we were sitting there is a sandy sward. It was an afternoon in early December, a winter's afternoon, with the warm winter sun of Pakistan shining and a feel of indolence in the air.

I say that we were sitting, and it is true of the other man, but as a matter of fact I was standing – in a circle that he had drawn for me in the sand. His task was to look after Mister Peacock and the others, and he said that he considered it his duty to look after me as well, since I had come to pay them a visit. I had a paper bag of meat with me, and a camera slung round my neck.

All about us was a wall of stone and crumbling mud, some eight feet high here on the inside, but rising no more than three feet or so from the level of the ground outside. There was a sort of exit to the outer world made up of rocks set against the wall by way of which a man could clamber out again. It did just cross my mind that it wasn't a very convenient exit, and to wonder why they had done nothing to make it easier. I asked the man about this and he explained that no one came in, in the ordinary way, except himself.

Terence hadn't come in. He was leaning over the wall behind me and well above where I stood in my circle, looking rather like the bust of a Roman emperor – except for his clothes. There were some villagers disposed along the wall beside him, and a wriggle of interest seemed to be stirring amongst them. Terence was interested too, I think – but in a different, more cerebral manner. I had seldom seen his features so immobile. As a rule he looks nothing like a Roman emperor's bust. The villagers had a look of their own, as if a long, empty afternoon lay ahead of them. I was a stranger and consequently amusing to look at. Something might happen. They had nut-brown faces. The people of this part of Pakistan, the majority of them Sindis or Mekranis, are seldom fair. These wore brightly coloured clothes – red and blue and green – and their eyes shone. One of them had a pink baseball cap, I remember, in the way one does remember little irrelevant details. I glanced along the line of them and then at Terence, who gave me a nod of encouragement.

The man by the pool was poking about with his wand at a pile of crocodiles, trying to isolate a particular one.

'There he is,' he said finally. 'There's Mister Peacock.'

Crocodiles like to lie about in heaps, as if they were spillikins – but heavier and less innocent. The one they call Mister Peacock is famous in the neighbourhood. He is the biggest and most splendid crocodile here, and some people consider him sacred. There is, however, still some controversy as to his true identity – whether he is really a peacock, or really a crocodile: so a compromise that allows of either possibility has been arrived at: people stick to his name, Mor sahib (which means Mister Peacock), and he continues to look for all the world like a crocodile; a crocodile, moreover, six hundred and something years old, for it is claimed that he arrived here in the thirteenth century with the intention of serving the saint whose tomb stands high on a rocky eminence above the pool enclosure. The saint's name is Mangho Pir.

There are a great many crocodiles, or peacocks or whatever they are, in the enclosure. Over a hundred, I reckon. They range from Mister Peacock himself, who is about fifteen feet long, to relatively young and small ones born to him this century or last. Big and small, they come out of their pool to sun themselves on the sand, like beached war-canoes. Nothing could be pleasanter for them than this fine pool set about with rocks. There are date-palms in clumps here and there, and a hot spring gushes out from

Mister Peacock

the base of the eminence on which Mangho Pir's shrine is built. The hot spring is magical and cures all sicknesses if you drink its waters or bathe in them. In earlier days sick pilgrims had to share the waters with Mister Peacock and his family, but this gave rise to ill-feeling on both sides and complaints and worse, and I am told that pilgrim attendance used to fall off every time there was a little incident, so in the end they put up the stone and mud wall. The sick can now take their ritual baths and draughts without having to concern themselves with anything but their cure and the prayers that accompany it. They are expected to make little ex-voto offerings to the saint after that, of course.

'That's Mister Peacock,' the man said again.

I dare say he thought I hadn't heard the first time, though as a matter of fact I had. The truth is that I was apprehensive – despite the peace and the warm indolence of the afternoon – and I thought it wise to remain silent. I could not remember (indeed, had I ever known?) whether crocodiles receive their impressions through their ears or their eyes, or their noses, or what. It wasn't that I was so nervous of Mister Peacock himself, because as anyone can see he is very old and somnolent; moreover the man was tapping his snout with his wand in a friendly way, so I assumed that he was not ill-disposed. But on three sides of me were other crocodiles, less old, more active, and almost as large as he. I had the disagreeable feeling that they were watching me. I was certainly watching them. I could have touched them – if I had wanted to.

I don't really know how I had found the courage to come down into their enclosure in the first place, unless it was that the man, their guardian, had told me to do so and had stared into my eyes with such contempt when he saw me hesitate. Terence had been rather unpleasant as well, reminding me that I had talked so loud and bold about what I planned to do. 'You keep on saying how much you like saints and their totem creatures,' he had said. So I had come in, and was standing silent and uneasy in my circle, nodding at the man. Yes, I could see perfectly: that one was Mister Peacock. There was no mistaking him – his majesty and his size alone would identify him. I had heard it said that he wore a vermilion mark on his forehead – a badge of rank – and I tried to occupy my mind with searching for it.

'And the vermilion mark?' I asked the man.

'The mark?'

He was leaning forward, looking for it, I suppose. Then he turned back to me and said: 'It's got rubbed off.'

Mister Peacock's eyes are like small unwinking stars, or French paste, and they are set very high in his head. When he floats lazily upon the waters, which he can do as easily as can logs of wood or submarines, he so arranges it that only his French-paste eyes and his nostrils are visible. If you look carefully, however, you may sometimes also see the tips of the machicolated ridges that outline the flatness of his back. These join together in a single jagged ridge towards the end of his tail. I couldn't see his tail at present: only his head, forelegs and the beginnings of his huge body, the rest being hidden still under some of the other crocodiles: but it was clear enough that he was Mister Peacock in person – and all those others were his progeny. The wall of stone and mud, as I have said, was eight feet high. Terence was safely beyond it, making gestures and noises of encouragement. The villagers looked very pleased now.

Meanwhile the guardian had taken a shorter hold of his wand and had started to stir the pile of crocodiles and after a moment of tumultuous heaving Mister Peacock managed to disengage himself and scramble forward onto the sand. Another crocodile tried to follow, but the man gave him a sharp rap with his wand on the snout and immediately there was a flailing of tails and a slamming of jaws as loud and hard and resonant as when you bang a succession of doors in anger. I think that Terence may have felt pity for me now. He was offering me comfort, and I pretended not to listen.

'Of course they are all perfectly tame,' he was saying, 'whatever ignorant people may say. And you *are* in your magic circle. Bear in mind that they're peacocks – and whoever heard of peacocks turning nasty? Swans, yes. Swans can break a man's leg with a blow from their wings, my nurse always used to tell me. I should just

Mister Peacock

keep perfectly calm, if I were you. You remember your first lesson in philosophy, about the distinction between appearance and reality? Well, apply it!' He paused and then said: 'How discoloured their teeth are.'

Terence was quite right about their teeth, though I chose to ignore him still. Their teeth were yellow, and there is also something else both interesting and disagreeable about them: the lower set are embedded in a jaw shaped like a bedpan, high at the back and lower in front, though the simile is not altogether accurate because bedpans are smooth and crocodiles' jaws are extremely irregular. Nevertheless you can see that the two sets of teeth, for all their irregularity, are designed to close very neatly, the upper and lower teeth interlocking with the accuracy of zip-fasteners. Mister Peacock was making his way over to me behind his guardian, quite fast, considering the weight of his years. I noticed that he had lost most of his teeth. It was a straw to cling to, in a way.

The man pointed round about, at Mister Peacock himself and at the others. Heaven knows how many there really were, floating about in the dark silence of the pool, apart from the group round me. 'Which one do you want?' he asked casually.

I stood considering the question.

'Choose one,' Terence said. 'Don't be nervous.'

I wanted to photograph them, it is true. Moreover I had wanted to photograph them so close that it would look as if they were at my very feet. I had spoken about this to Terence on the way here, perhaps a little presumptuously, and this may have been the reason why he was being so remorseless from the top of his eight-foot wall. Well, I had got my wish. They were at my very feet, and their eyes were open. So were mine. It only remained for me to focus my camera as well as my eyes.

'That one ...' I said after a moment. My voice had come out smaller than I had expected.

In choosing my first victim I had deliberately ignored all the crocodiles at my feet and had chosen one some few yards away – though at least twelve feet long: one whose face happened to be

13

pointing towards the pool. The middle of his body was behind a date-palm growing near the water. If the creature started to move when the guardian stirred him (and I knew instinctively that this was what the man would do) it would perhaps make for the water. I assumed it would make for the water, anyway. And if it flailed with its tail it would strike its companions, who were armoured against such risks, or the date-palm. It had great length but only four little feet, so it would take time to round the tree if it chose to come in my direction. This was my second assumption, in case the first proved wrong.

'Go on,' Terence said. 'Have you no faith in magic?'

'That one,' I repeated, in a loud, strong voice.

The guardian skipped across several creatures and gave my chosen crocodile a great beat over the snout. These were all snub-nosed crocodiles, by the way: not gharials, which have long, attenuated noses – though this is a distinction I did not consider at the time. But I had proved quite right in my judgement. The crocodile struck out with its tail, threw the forepart of its body into the air and snapped with its jaws. Then it shot forward into the water. It was astonishing with what speed it was able to do all this. I photographed it as it did it, but the camera must have moved somehow, and the picture has turned out to be of almost nothing but palm-fronds.

'Did you get it?' Terence asked. 'You know that some people say crocodiles never attack a man in the winter? A strange idea.'

Mister Peacock was coming closer and he had his mouth open. I felt obliged to say something, so I said:

'The insides of their mouths are white, like veal.'

Crocodiles very often leave their mouths open, but I had the idea that Mister Peacock was expecting to have some meat put into his. Since the stone and mud wall was built, the crocodiles at Mangho Pir's shrine have had to rely very largely upon well-wishers for their food, whereas before they at least stood some chance of catching things for themselves. That's what made ritual bathing such a nerve-racking performance in the old days: but against that, people say that in the old days the crocodiles were very well disciplined and only rarely forgot that they were not supposed to touch the pilgrims. They haven't had a pilgrim for years and years now and although I admit they were behaving well (except when the man stirred them), I was not sure of them.

Yet I was a good deal more collected by now than I had been at first. If Mister Peacock had been a tenth of his actual size I dare say I would even have found him endearing: but in any case my situation was so improbable that I had begun to question the reality of it – all those ridiculous crocodiles, too many for truth: a hundred and more, all made of silvery leather, the insides of their mouths veal-white. They never eat men in the winter? Very well, but who could be sure it was winter today, with that hot sun and that hot spring perpetually disclaiming it? In Sind you cannot count on calendars or the goodwill of crocodiles. But I pulled myself together again and said:

'I had hoped the insides of their mouths would be vermilion; and then realised that it would seem a stupid thing to say, so I explained: 'I'm using colour film, you see. I need colour.'

'You don't like the insides of their mouths?' the man asked. He was annoyed, I think.

'No, he doesn't,' Terence replied for me.

'Oh well,' the man said, and out of pure spite smacked at a crocodile immediately beside me.

It snapped with its jaws, I jumped, the man laughed, Terence had the grace to gasp, and all the crocodiles began hissing, for this is the noise they make when seriously provoked. An appalling hiss, like steam-engines.

The man must have decided that he had gone too far and he tried to make amends. 'They only mean to tease,' he said. 'There,' he went on, redrawing my magic circle, which had become a bit blurred because of my shuffling feet. 'There! That's better, isn't it?'

Is it? Was it? I wanted only to be done with all this and go. So I drew myself up again and said: 'What about a bit of meat? Please put some into one of those open mouths. That one, for instance.'

'No. Not that one. First for Mister Peacock.'

I had particularly not wanted Mister Peacock because he has so few teeth and in any case was rather too close for me to focus properly. But I was in the man's hands and he took my paper bag and divided some of the meat into several little pieces. One or two of them he then tossed into Mister Peacock's mouth which was waiting for it. Then he poked the meat back into the creature's gullet with his wand. As soon as he had done this Mister Peacock seemed ready to swallow it. I am not sure if he was so old that he couldn't manipulate things with his tongue, or if he was too grand to try: but in either case I was angry with myself for having been afraid and for having shown it. So I took a few photographs with studied unconcern, to prove that I was now master of the situation.

'More meat,' the man said.

I handed him the paper bag again. He took some meat out of it and handed the bag back. Terence had started a speech. He is not accustomed to remaining so silent so long. I listened to him with one ear, and watched with one eye as the man tossed a bit of meat into another mouth – a mouth all teeth that would gladly bite off a man's leg at the hip whereas they had nothing to bite on at present but a miserable little bit of meat the size of a matchbox. 'In the eighteen-eighties …' Terence was saying.

'In the eighteen-eighties – or perhaps the nineties: the records don't give the exact date – a sergeant in the 33rd Regiment (the Duke of Wellington's) came to Mangho Pir with his camera. That was back in the days when cameras had to be mounted on tripods because their lenses weren't fast enough for what you, or crocodiles for that matter, would call "snapshots". This brave sergeant had come to photograph Mister Peacock.'

I made no comment.

'Well,' Terence continued, 'this sergeant had set up his apparatus and wriggled into the black-velvet balldress that went with such things in his day and was peering at the image of Mister Peacock on his ground-glass screen. And suddenly one of the other crocodiles let out with its tail and knocked the little group sideways into the sand. Oddly enough the sergeant was not much

Mister Peacock

hurt – because of all his black-velvet swaddlings, I dare say. But he was more than ever determined. So he set up his apparatus again and he got his photograph. I can show you a reproduction of it in a book of the period.'

'Is it a good photograph?' I asked, trying to seem glad to hear about this sergeant in the 33rd.

'No, it isn't,' Terence said. 'And Sir Richard Burton came here too, you know. But that was in the eighteen-forties, before the days of cameras. Anyway, Sir Richard Burton made Mister Peacock's acquaintance: and it's interesting to consider that Mister Peacock is probably the only creature living today that can claim to have met Sir Richard.'

It was time to make a stand. 'I hope to be the only creature living today that can claim to have met Mister Peacock on his own ground,' I said. I did not wish to share my experience with the sergeant of the 33rd or Sir Richard, distinguished as they might be: in any case, I did not wish to share it at the very moment of experiencing it.

'More meat,' the man said.

'There *is* no more meat,' I said, looking into the bag.

'No more meat,' the man said softly, almost as if to himself. Then he looked at me in a peculiar way.

He turned and pointed to a crocodile immediately behind me, and I turned too. There were two of them there, but the one he was pointing at was by far the larger of the two – and to be honest I had not realised that there was even one there, between me and the emergency exit.

'That one – that big one with his mouth and teeth: he is begging you for meat so that he may not starve. It is days since he had some good meat. Ten rupees would be enough to buy meat for him. Please give ten rupees and I will at once arrange.'

Ten rupees was a pound sterling – not very much when you consider how the poor starving creature was waiting there with its mouth open.

A ten-rupee note fluttered down from above.

'It would have been worth ten times ten rupees,' Terence said, putting his wallet back into his pocket. 'It has been most instructive. I hope you've been taking notes.'

* * *

A few minutes later we were clambering up to Mangho Pir's shrine to put an offering in his alms-box.

'Mister Peacock would make a very nice opening chapter for you, Peter,' Terence said. 'I offer you the suggestion. You can open with Mister Peacock, move on to Mangho Pir, and from Mangho Pir as a particular saint to Muslim saints in general. In Chapter Two you can then go straight into an excursus on Islamic mysticism. Chapter Three can start with ...'

I interrupted him: 'He's too Barnum and Bailey. Too circus-trick.'

'Too circus-trick? Mangho Pir? But surely ...'

'I meant Mister Peacock. But Mangho Pir, up there in his shrine: I don't myself believe that he should count as a true saint, any more than I can accept Mister Peacock as a sacred creature.'

'You're splitting hairs. You say you want to write a treatise on saints and pirs and Sufism and the Islamic mystics generally. You need an opening chapter, and I offer you a perfect opening chapter.'

'But I *don't* keep on saying I want to write a treatise on pirs or on anything else! I said I wanted to try something easy about dervishes and faqirs.'

'And how can you hope to do even that without an excursus on mysticism?'

'Well, I suppose I'd have to put in a frieze of saints and pirs,' I admitted, rather throwing them away as if they were of no importance. Actually I didn't want to talk about it at all, at present.

We had reached the top of Mangho Pir's rocky eminence by now. You get a panoramic view of the countryside from here, but the countryside is depressing. If it were not for the oasis of date-palms and crocodiles and the shrine surmounting it, the eye would travel miserably through three hundred and sixty degrees of desolation, too squat for majesty, too parched, too spirit-haunted, too seamed with little graves. There is nothing on which an eye, or a bird, would gladly settle. Nor is the shrine itself worth more than a fleeting visit. It's courtyard is pretty, however – and filled with cats and old women. At a time when I lived for a while in Karachi I used to come to Mangho Pir occasionally and on each visit I had been struck by the sunk-ribbed emptiness of his cats and beggarwomen. To offer them a penny was like offering one's fingers to a handful of fishhooks. It was better to drop a coin into the alms-box and to hope that some needy stomach would benefit.

We dropped our coins in and Terence said: 'Why have you taken so against poor Mangho Pir?'

'But I haven't taken against him at all. I admire and respect him. He was clearly a very fine and pious old hermit, back there in the thirteenth century. But it's dervishes and faqirs that I like. Mangho Pir has none to speak of. You can't call Mister Peacock's guardian a dervish – and I don't like him anyhow. No. The truth is that Mangho Pir isn't a real saint, I'm afraid. Saints in Islam are just as much under the obligation to work miracles as saints in Christendom, surely. Otherwise they aren't true saints. And who, may I ask, performed all the miracles hereabouts? Who caused his toothbrush twig to turn itself into an oasis of date-palms? Not Mangho Pir. And who smacked at the rock with his wand and produced a perennial spring of water at a temperature of one hundred and thirty-three degrees Fahrenheit? Not Mangho Pir.'

'And who,' broke in Terence – on his mettle now, no doubt because of my fluent documentation – 'metamorphosed a little wilting flower into Mister Peacock?'

'A flower?'

I was rather taken aback.

'Yes, a flower.'

'But I'd always heard that Mister Peacock was miraculously summoned from the Indus, and that he walked here – or flew, possibly: it depends upon which way you care to think of him – in order to serve Mangho Pir.'

'Nothing of the sort,' Terence said. 'At least, the best authorities think not. Mister Peacock was a little wilting flower until twelve hundred and something. You must be careful to check your facts, Peter.'

'Whatever the case,' I said, 'it was not Mangho Pir who did all these good and useful miracles, was it? And that's the point I'm trying to make. Incidentally there was a fourth miracle as well – though I can't remember what it was for the moment. Each of the Four Friends worked a little miracle for Mangho Pir's sake. He was so wretchedly uncomfortable here until the Four Friends took pity on him: no water, no greenery, no crocodiles to do his bidding. I fear it's obvious that Mangho Pir could do no miracles himself. In fact he was just a hermit, not a saint.'

'Miracles of that sort are what saints do for other people,' Terence reminded me. 'It would not have been right for him to do it for himself.'

We were already in the car again, having left the shrine and the hill it is built on. Terence was driving, in silence for a few hundred yards, and then he suddenly emerged from a private reverie and said: 'Good. So let us say that you plan to open with Mangho Pir and Mister Peacock. You will then fan outwards to each of the Four Friends, whoever they may be. And from the Four Friends you will embark upon the great open seas of Mysticism. Is that it? An excellent plan. Now, please, identify the Four Friends.'

I hesitated. 'I don't think I can – with any certainty. But Qalandar Lal Shah Baz was one of them, they say.'

'None better. The great Qalandar. And his date fits too. Thirteenth century. You've visited his shrine at Sehwan Sharif, of course.'

'Never. But I'm going. I feel strongly about the Qalandar.'

'Possibly my favourite saint in the whole of Sind,' Terence announced. 'Next?'

'Well, some people think that Shah Abdul Latif of ...'

'Shah Abdul Latif of Bhit!' He went rigid behind the steering-wheel. Terence may be the oldest and best of friends but he is also a cobra when it comes to striking down an inaccuracy. So he struck:

'Nonsense! What on earth can you be thinking of? Shah Abdul Latif is eighteenth century. An admirable saint – I agree wholeheartedly there: but more than four hundred years out of the question!'

'It isn't me thinking of anything, Terence,' I told him wearily. 'It's what people say. And if crocodiles we had always supposed were peacocks prove in reality to be little wilting flowers, then surely we need not boggle at a trifling readjustment of Time! Time isn't anything so naïve as months and years marked off on a slate, after all.'

He closed his lips and nodded, and continued nodding when he had reopened them to start upon what he had to say. 'All right. Do as you think fit. Include Shah Abdul Latif. You'll have the experts down on you like tigers, but ignore them! And don't say afterwards that I didn't warn you.'

It was now more than ever difficult to return to my own ground, but I tried, as lightly as possible: 'As a matter of fact I shall not be including Shah Abdul Latif.'

'Don't mind me. Carry on – include him, for all I care.'

'No. I shall not be using him,' I said – but I lacked the face to give the true reason for leaving him out.

Shah Abdul Latif of Bhit is probably the most considerable figure in the history of eighteenth-century Sind – poet, philosopher, saint, mystic, spiritual guide: but it happens that he doesn't appeal to me, and the point is to choose the saints you like, and everyone chooses his own favourites to make up the Four Friends. The Friends only seem to come into Mangho Pir's story as bolsters for him – because he needs bolstering. Qalandar Lal Shah Baz and Shah Abdul Latif are the two most commonly included in the list, because they are two of the most popular saints in Sind: and the remaining two are any other two you happen to like personally. They could be as late for the rendezvous as Shah Abdul Latif and it would not matter. It was pure accident, anyhow, that the great Qalandar's dates fit in, as we choose to reckon time. But as a matter of fact I had decided not to use Mangho Pir either, so there was really no point in using his bolster-saints as such: nor need I identify them. I did not tell Terence this. Instead I said:

'I must have a frieze of saints – I can see that. And to start with I choose Qalandar Lal Shah Baz.'

'And after him?' Terence inquired in a flat voice.

'I'm not sure yet. I've got a little list of visits I want to make.'

He made a sudden volte-face, charmingly and with no apparent effort. 'I see. And it sounds to me a very sensible way of doing things. Moreover if you should want a good, *small* saint – who's never been much in the public eye, I believe – let me commend Ghazi Baba to you. He has the advantage of being very near to hand, too. Right here in Karachi. My orderly tells me that his wife has just had a male child by Ghazi Baba's kind intervention, after years and years of unsuccessful struggle on his own account. He insists, by the way, that Ghazi Baba is eighth-century, which would be very, very early for a Muslim saint – but I was forgetting. Dates don't come into it.'

'How did dates come into your orderly's conversation?' I asked with interest.

'They didn't, of course. He merely remarked that Ghazi Baba arrived in Sind with Muhammad bin Qasim the Arab conqueror – and that would make him very early eighth-century, AD 711, to be exact.'

I could see Terence's eyes glistening behind his sunglasses, and his voice turned soft and silken as he continued. 'What if Ghazi Baba should prove to be one of the Four Friends? He might well have been – if you find that you like him. It seems a pity to throw away so remarkable a possibility – could you not use the Four Friends after all? You could join them in friendship and separate them by the centuries.' He looked me blandly between the eyes and the car lurched dizzily. 'It's only a suggestion, naturally,' he said as he swung the steering wheel over. 'It's your book.'

* * *

All that was very shortly after my arrival in Pakistan that winter.

A few days later I was dining with Terence in Karachi and he returned to the subject of saints and pirs, but in a strange, ambivalent mood. He was much worried on my account.

'It's a highly complex subject, you see, Peter,' he said – and then hurried on before pride could force a protest out of me. 'Don't misunderstand. I don't mean that it should be the exclusive preserve of the tigers: but you're rather asking for trouble if you mean to go in amongst them all and chatter away about *dhikr* and *sama* and *boruz* and *tawakkul* and ...'

'... and *shath* and *fana f-il-haqiqat* and *baqa*,' I put in quickly, stringing out three of them in line because I was determined to show that I knew the terms too – but I was stuck for a moment at *baqa*. 'And *baqa*,' I repeated, temporising and trying to remember what could come next, till suddenly *lahūt* skimmed like a little comet across my mind, so I put that in too: '*Lahūt* comes next, doesn't it?' He looked up in a way that suggested to me for one triumphant second that he didn't know, so I said slyly: 'Or haven't you come across *lahūt*?'

'And Neoplatonism and Gnosis and the Manichees,' Terence continued, unruffled: ' – and of course I know about *lahūt*: I can also tell you that it does come next. It's the state that follows *baqa* in the progress towards complete annihilation of self, where all the adept's actions – all, all: his movements, his twitchings, his cries, everything – are directly inspired by God.'

'Good,' I said, a little disappointed. 'I wasn't quite sure. I thought that perhaps there was another intermediary state – *holūl*, or something – where ...'

'In that case you'll do better not to think,' Terence said. 'I *know*.'

'And I *gnose*.'

For a moment Terence congealed into the Roman emperor. 'With a "g"?'

'With a "g",' I said.

But did he after all intend this talk to be serious?

'My dear Peter,' he said, a speech from the throne this time: 'Don't tell me that you're going to lay claim to an inspired gnostic revelation simply because you happen to like dirty old men in rags who say they're dervishes!' We looked at each other and suddenly he laughed. 'All I meant was that you should be careful with your metaphysics,' he said.

'Alas …'

I sat thinking and he sat watching.

Then I said: 'I was rather hoping, since dervishes manage to do very well without metaphysics, that I might be allowed to do without them too. But it would be nice to throw some of the words in – just for good measure and abracadabra.'

'Certainly – so long as the words don't appear to mean anything,' he agreed. Then he leant forward, looking pleased. 'But on the other hand, if you said your plan was to go dancing with the dervishes, that would be quite different. None of the tigers in the field has been much of a dancer, from what I've read.' He helped himself to some fruit – we had practically finished dinner by now, and the servant was bringing in coffee and brandy and cigars. 'It's a dullish dance, I fear: just round and round on the left heel for hour after hour until ecstasy supervenes. Ecstasy or exhaustion. It sometimes takes all night for that to happen.'

'The Moulawyya, you mean? But are there any of the Moulawyya confraternity in Sind? I believe not. So I shall be spared their dizzy whirling.'

'A pity, but never mind. Singing with the dervishes, then. There are plenty of spiritual concerts in Sind, anyway.'

'I don't think they'll let me. At least the true ascetics won't. It's not just like joining a glee-club. They say that in the really exclusive confraternities there's a novitiate of a thousand and one nights before the poor battered novice can hope to be allowed to take part. That means nearly three years of emptying slops and sweeping floors, after all.'

He fixed me with beady good-humour. 'If they don't dance, and won't let you sing with them – or eat glass, or snakes, or cut yourself and decline to bleed, or froth, or fall, or whatever the ecstatic speciality may be – then kindly tell me how you propose to spend your evenings. You'll simply be left outside, with no ecstasy and without even the chilly comforts of metaphysics to console you.'

We sat sipping our coffee for a few moments, Terence still fixing me with his beads, and with me trying to prepare my defence.

'Well?'

And I said: 'I'm a little bewildered, it's true – partly by your conversation and partly by my own temerity. Metaphysics? I must leave them to the tigers: what I want are the dervishes – and I honestly am much drawn towards them: dervishes as men, not metaphysicians. I had an idea that it would be interesting to spend some more time with them, here in Sind. After all, Sind is wonderfully rich in dervishes.'

'First things first,' said Terence. 'Dervishes come later, and not even next. What about the saints?'

* * *

H. Lammens has put it very succinctly in one of his studies.[1] The Qoran admits of no reciprocity between the Creator and His creation. The concept of the Love of God is inconceivable in Islam, for 'love' implies the idea of gift and countergift (of reciprocity, in fact, and this is out of the question). To seek union with God is meaningless, consequently. Between God and man there can be no direct communication, and any attempt to bridge the gap is branded as a polytheistic maoeuvre (a resiling, as it were, from the unshakeable monotheism of Islam). Nor can the soul look to any intermediary in the struggle to ensure its salvation. These are the orthodox rulings that Lammens quotes – for the fact is that saints and saint-cults are violently and fundamentally opposed to the basic teachings of Islam – of the Qoran and the Sunna, that is to say.

But as everyone very well knows, humanity has from the beginning sought to narrow the distance between God and its wretched self – and Muslim humanity has been no exception, despite the uncompromising dogma of the Qoran and Sunna. So Muslims have tried too – by prayer, by detachment from the world, by vigils rather on the lines of the early Christian monks, by asceticism, by the mystic discipline of *tassawūf* (the *Sūfi* principles), by spiritual exercises sometimes of the most fantastic sort – the

1. *L'Islam: croyances et institutions.* 3rd edition. Beyrouth, 1943.

self-mutilations, the chantings, the mortifications of the flesh – till you had men like Hosein bin Mansur al-Hallaj crying out 'I AM THE TRUTH!' and claiming to have attained unity with the Divine Essence – the oneness, *Ittihad*. Orthodox Islam was obliged to take action. Al-Hallaj was taken, flogged, mutilated, hung from a gibbet and finally beheaded after his death. This was in the tenth century. There were many others, some of them earlier, but most later: Jalaluddin Rumi, the Persian, for example. It was he who said:

'To say I AM HE at the wrong moment (as Pharaoh did) is a curse;

'But to say I AM HE at the right moment (as did Mansur) is a blessing.'

It was Jalaluddin who founded the Moulawyya, that confraternity of dervishes with their dizzy whirling of which we had been speaking earlier that evening.

Such men as these took a deep hold on the imagination. Small wonder that orthodox Islam was alarmed, but the cult of saints – intermediaries, as they seemed, between man and the almost-unreachable Godhead – spread slowly outwards, particularly amongst the peoples of Persia and of the subcontinent of India, peoples who were so much more disposed towards the esoteric mysteries than were the Arabs who had conquered and converted millions of their numbers to Islam.

Even so, the mysteries were not for the many and when, long after, a Javanese follower of al-Hallaj cried out in his ecstasy 'I AM GOD!' he was arrested and brought before a court to answer for his crime. His judges ruled that the accused had probably been right in his claim – there were indications that at the moment of making it, he *had* achieved *Ittihad*, the oneness with the Divinity. They acquitted him, finding him guilty only of 'having announced a truth too sublime for earthly intelligence', a truth he ought to have kept to himself.

By the end of the twelfth century AD, five hundred years or so after the revelation of the Qoran to the Prophet Muhammad, saints and saint-cults were an established feature of Islam, and remain so to this day. The shrines of saints are centres of pilgrimage and in the

Mister Peacock

East a special element is added – the concept that the spirit and the blessedness of the original saint can be transmitted to his son and to his son's son, to a line of hereditary saints, as it were, inheritors in perpetuity of all that the original saint had stood for. This was not an entirely new concept, for despite Islam's truly democratic framework, the person of the great Prophet Muhammad and the persons of his family and descendants, the Syeds and the Sharifs, had from the outset been granted a patent of spiritual nobility. Nor should this seem strange to the peoples of the West, because it is really no more than a parallel to the concept of the Divine Right of Kings, which is clear to most people whether they subscribe to it or not. A man becomes a king, by conquest or whatever it may be, but in any event for reasons connected with his personal qualities. He founds a dynasty in which his sons succeed him by simple virtue of their birth. So also with these saints: you have a line of hereditary saints, of men as good, bad or indifferent as Kings have been, of great personal qualities or of none. The living saint in Islam is what he is precisely because of his inheritance and because of the veneration in which his followers hold him on that account. He is the pir – the saint – the sitter-on-the-throne, or *gadinisshin* (the Persian term is used in the East). Sometimes he wields enormous power.

It is a very widespread practice amongst Muslims in the East for a man to attach himself to some pir whom he will regard as his spiritual adviser, and most probably there will be some family connection with this same pir, the man's father having perhaps owed allegiance to him as *murid*, too. *Murid* would mean 'disciple' or 'follower', and follower is the better word, for the ordinary *murid* is not required to give much more than lip-service to his pir, and a contribution in the collection-plate every so often. It is different with the dervishes. The dervishes are the people of the Way. Monks, possibly. Dedicated men. Something more is demanded of them either by their pir or by their own consciences, or both: almost an act of renunciation. If you believe that the Way leads them to God through the intermediary of the pir, then God is their reward. If you don't believe this, then you must suppose that they get nothing in return for their dedicated lives – though there is, of course, a third possibility: that the lives of a great many dervishes are not dedicated at all and that they themselves are no better than idle mountebanks. In such cases it is not a spiritual rapture that they enjoy but the emptiness of lives freed from all responsibility. Their stomachs are filled (partly, in any case) by the offerings that their pir's followers make, or else by whoever passes by – for the giving of alms is one of the five pillars of Islam, and there is no shame in begging. Nor is the beggar grateful to the giver. His gratitude is reserved for God.

We had been talking of all this that evening, and Terence now said:

'What do you think of that kind of dervish?'

'The mountebank kind?'

'Yes.'

I didn't answer at once, so Terence jogged me on:

'You don't find them rather empty?'

I did not want to commit myself. Finally I said: 'That kind can always fill themselves up with *bhang*.'

'Bunged up with *bhang*,' Terence said contemplatively. 'Hashish. Hm-m. Have a brandy,' he said in a different voice.

'Thank you.'

'Perhaps I'll have some too.'

He pushed the bottle over to me. After a moment he said:

'You're off to Sehwan Sharif tomorrow and you haven't even taken the trouble to visit Ghazi Baba.'

'Oh but I have!' I told him. 'I went the day before yesterday – the day after you told me about him. But the *gadi-nisshin* was out – he was invisible, anyway. There was no one there at all except a dervish with a cockatoo in his hair.'

'What did he say?'

'The dervish? Nothing. Nor the cockatoo.'

'And you?'

'I?'

I leaned back and remembered. 'I was speechless with horror – polite, social horror. I didn't even go up into the shrine, but stopped on the steps that lead to it. They're in the middle of rebuilding, so that what was before a modest little place perched on a rock is now going to look like a provincial movie-house. A small one. Even the tree with its load of votive dolls' cradles (your orderly's wife's offering amongst them, no doubt) is not to be spared. It looks as if they were planning to give it a surround of terrazzo tiling.'

'It sounds as if Ghazi Baba were a very successful saint, then.'

'They're spending a lot of money, anyhow. He must have a very rich and grateful clientèle. I came away quickly. No,' I said with finality. 'Qalandar Lal Shah Baz is the one for me. By this time tomorrow …'

2
A Cushion in the Skies

THERE IS NOTHING DIFFICULT about the journey to Sehwan. I have come by train. If I had had a car, I could equally well have come by road. Travel in the Indus Valley is in fact easy enough wherever communications exist; but even today, in the twentieth century, the road and rail systems are rudimentary.

You can travel by rail from Karachi up the right bank of the river Indus (as I have done as far as Sehwan) or up the left bank through Hyderabad, the Sindi capital, to where the river is bridged again and the two principal branches of the railway meet at Rohri Junction. Beyond Rohri the railway leaves the Indus, one line crossing very soon into the Punjab, another making for the mountains of Baluchistan. Then there are roads, of course: notably the main trunk road from Karachi through Hyderabad to Rohri and on to Lahore, and another route that would take you eventually to Quetta, but neither Quetta nor Lahore concerns my narrative. There are the little internal tributary roads, too. Alternatively you could sail on the broad surface of the river Indus, if you wanted to – in river-craft that have outlandish names, such as *doondee* and *zorakh*, and strange high-stemmed silhouettes – but the river is really only navigable in the season when the snows are melting on the roof of the world, up in the distant Himalayas: and that means during a season of stifling, terrifying heat in the Indus Valley. Nobody moves in the summer unless he must.

So long as you stick to the main routes, it is all quite easy. It is when you leave them that progress slows down to four legs or two, or to the creaking of bullock-cart wheels. In general, even today, the

Sindi people keep to their restricted village worlds and, for them, such city names as Karachi, Hyderabad, Sukkur, are no more than the shimmering of a mirage over the horizons of their experience.

I have been here in Sehwan since evening – yesterday evening, perhaps I should say, because it is now well past midnight.

It was already dusk when the train stopped, so I have seen nothing yet of the countryside and almost nothing of the little town. The station was lit by a few inadequate oil-lamps. This was true of many of the wayside stations from dusk onwards as we came chugging through the broken foot-hill country up the right bank of the Indus, and at one of them I jumped down onto the platform and asked the guard where we were and how many stations ahead Sehwan would be. I was afraid that I might easily pass through it without realising that I had arrived at my destination. He counted on his fingers – hm ... hm ... '... oh yes, and Amni. Three. And the fourth from here is Sehwan.'

So I counted them as we came along and deduced that this must be the place. The writing on the lamp-glasses was illegible, and I could see no name-board anywhere, though perhaps there would be one at the end of the platform, where the engine could see it. One or two other passengers got out as well, but there appeared to be no coolies to handle the luggage, unless the man with a sort of loop in his hand was a coolie. A loop. A lasso?

A whip. And the man was a tonga-driver. Now that my eyes were becoming better used to the darkness, I could even see his horse beyond the platform palings, and his two-wheeled tonga behind it.

'This *is* Sehwan?' I asked him, to confirm my counting.

'But of course!' He was surprised. If you are in Sehwan, of course you are in Sehwan. He waved his whip in the direction of his tonga. 'You want tonga?'

We loaded my baggage and I climbed in too.

Then we set off. Away to the left I could see a few small yellow lights, possibly a mile distant. It must be the town – the oldest inhabited town-site in Sind. For the moment we were in the midst

A Cushion in the Skies

of a dark, invisible jungle, as far as I could determine. If there had been a moon, perhaps it would have struck a gleam from the waters of the Indus, somewhere far below us to the south-east.

'Where shall I take you?' the driver asked.

It was time to face this problem squarely. Hitherto I had evaded it. Some days ago, in Karachi, a distinguished citizen gave me an introduction to Pir Gul Muhammad Shah of Sehwan Sharif – *gadi-nisshin* of the great Qalandar Lal Shah Baz. He did not actually give me a letter, as a matter of fact, but it came to the same thing, he said, because he was writing to Pir sahib to warn him of my coming. No dates were named. 'Dates', in the sense of engagements, are scarcely worth naming, Time being what it is in Sind. But he assured me that Pir sahib would welcome me whenever I chose to come to him. With some part of my brain, the part that can respond to Eastern stimuli, I knew this might be true: but in another part of my brain were flashes of doubt, like fireflies, illuminating their own behinds and nothing else.

'Is there a Dak Bungalow?' I asked the man, doubtfully.

'There is a Rest House.'

A Rest House differs from a Dak Bungalow both in its magnificence and in its purpose. A Rest House is ordinarily reserved for officials on duty, or for people who have been given a special permit to occupy it. A Dak Bungalow is often rather mean – but it is open to all comers and at least offers them a roof over their heads.

'I have no permit,' I said. 'Is there a cook there? I can find food and a bed?'

'I don't know. You wish me to take you to the Rest House?'

'No,' I said emphatically, extinguishing the last of the fireflies. 'To the house of Pir Gul Muhammad Shah sahib.'

'Ah-h!' The tonga-man was impressed and turned to peer more closely at me. 'Good.'

Ten minutes later, through dark and dust and the prickly smell of dust, we rumbled under a municipal arch of WELCOME and were in the town. A few lamplit booths were open still and at an occasional corner an oil-lamp glimmered. It was agreeably cold – much colder than Karachi on the coast – and I was glad of my greatcoat. The town had an air of having been looted and partly destroyed. Many of the houses seemed in ruins, many others shuttered and barricaded. Once or twice we passed a scurrying wayfarer and were greeted by him and questioned and he would be told where I was going: but to all intents and purposes the town might already be in its grave or in a trance resembling death. For the length of a narrow street we drove uphill, and then rounded a corner on to the flat again. We drove up to an arched gateway, more or less closed.

'Here,' the tonga-man said, climbing down into the dust.

I had had time to prepare my speech. I said:

'Go in and tell Pir sahib that an Englishman has come to visit him – the Englishman who has been named in a letter that he will already have received, *Insha 'Allah* – if God wills.'

He seemed quite satisfied and went in, without knocking.

A minute or so later he was back again, preceded by another man I could scarcely see in the darkness; rather a heavy man, I think, with a skin fair enough to be distinguished from the night, but I cannot go farther than that. Another man, much smaller and very much darker, followed them, carrying a lantern. They examined me under its beam. I made the sort of smile that I hoped would strike them as self-assured yet friendly. I am not certain if I succeeded: I think perhaps not, because they left me thereupon, without speaking, and came back with yet another man, who looked me over still more carefully. I was too busy being looked at to take proper note of their faces.

The last man evidently had more confidence in his judgement than the other two. '*Aiyye*,' he said, in Urdu. 'Please come.'

I was relieved. The letter had worked, in the first place; and in the second there was at least one man here who could speak Urdu. I have since discovered, of course, that several others can too. I don't speak Sindi, and though I have been at pains to conceal my fears even from myself, I have been wondering whether Urdu, the *lingua franca* of Pakistan, will in fact suffice, so far from the big towns. In

A Cushion in the Skies

the big towns, naturally: and with such people as tonga-drivers and others who look to visitors for part of their living. But in remote though holy Sehwan – it could well be very different.

I went in with the man and he left me standing alone in a courtyard while he directed the assembling of my bits of baggage. There was a clump of small trees and shrubs ahead of me with some animals sleeping under them. Probably goats. Beyond this was a low, one-storeyed building, rather ramshackle, and perhaps outhouses of some kind. To my right, beyond a praying-place that gleamed luminously white, was a colonnade of darkish pillars, hung with reed screens through which light shone in horizontal rays. There was a silence beyond the screens that suggested not emptiness but people holding their breath.

Then the baggage came in from the tonga, and the man carrying it motioned to me to follow him, turning left at the entrance and making for the other end of the courtyard. I followed him obediently and was faced with a wall, set at right angles to the alley by which we had approached the house. The wall was highish at one end, with a parapet; and at the other end it dropped to a mere six foot or so, pierced by a door. The little dark man with the lantern hurried forward to reach the door before I did, and opened it.

I wasn't expected tonight, rather than on any other night. No one was actually expected. So it was an agreeable surprise to discover that the little house they now opened up for me was kept ready for occupation. In Sind they call such guesthouses *otāq*; they are set aside for guests and insulated from the main house by a courtyard (as in this case), or by a wall or some other physical barrier.

This particular otaq has its own small patio, with a colonnade fronting the building. The building has one long room with as many windows and doors as there are arches to the colonnade – three doors and two windows, as a matter of fact. The little man with the lantern was already in the room ahead of the rest of us, and crouching in one of the corners. He was fiddling with something, and after a short delay a second lamp lit itself with a vagrant yellow flame that licked and swayed. Soon the flame seemed to control itself, and turned red. The man began pumping madly; the red turned orange, then yellow, and began to hiss and splutter till all at once it exploded in a violent cone of light and was carried triumphantly to an embrasure behind the sofa.

'Please be seated,' they said, indicating the sofa, and left me.

So I sat.

The room is very pleasant: about twelve feet deep and perhaps twenty-five long, but I do not like petrol-vapour lamps and never hope to. I admit that they give a very powerful light, but it is hard and unrelenting and I suffer from the fear that at any moment now it will burst its bonds and surround me with liquid fire as undisciplined and mad as floodwaters. Or else it will go out and leave me benighted. I moved from my corner of the sofa to the other end and put five more feet between me and the lamp. It continued to roar threateningly.

I went on sitting on that sofa for a very long time, my three front doors and two windows before me. On my left an immense bed on spindle legs of lacquer: scarlet, with rings of parrot-pink and parrot-green and some little flowers painted on them here and there. Three quite plump strangers could bed down in that bed without embarrassment or overlapping, or four at a pinch – and they could all be over six-foot-something without their toes hanging over the end of it. I sat considering this terrible image for a bit, till my mind was distracted by movement in the patio. A head peeped round a column and quickly withdrew itself.

My bed has two silk coverlets, the lower of the two fastened to the tops of the bed-legs with a criss-crossing of scarlet cords. The cords have gold bobbles at the end of them. There is a bolster with a coloured silk cover and a lace fringe. I said to myself: 'That bolster has a hard look.' On top of everything is a *razāi*. Razais are a commonplace of the Pakistani night. They are huge quilts, big enough to roll yourself in from head to foot with a great deal over at each end, and width to spare for a second turn round your body. They are filled with teased cotton, and one good razai is the equivalent in warmth of two, possibly three, normal woollen

A Cushion in the Skies

blankets. The Sindi razais are, I think, the loveliest in the whole country. Mine gives the impression of patchwork, though it is really a form of appliqué work. The central panel is black, with heraldic shapes appliqué'd to it in white – things that look like formalised choppers and swords. Framing this central panel is a series of narrow borders in yellow and orange and white: and framing the internal borders is a very wide final border in unrelieved black again. It pleased me very much and I got up to feel it – and took this opportunity of confirming that the bolster is just as hard as it looks – and someone immediately coughed in the patio outside. Perhaps he thought I was asleep all the while I was sitting motionless on the sofa and now saw that I was not. He coughed again.

'Come in!' I called.

A head flicked round a column and out of sight again. Its place was instantly taken by another, which disappeared too.

'Come in!'

One of them came in. He was the smallest of those I have seen so far, the one who had carried the lantern: very small and young and dark, and he had thick curly black hair – not frizzed, but close curls; rather what a Negro might be expected to have if his hair were to grow to a length of six inches and then twist back on itself as tightly as could be against the scalp. He wore a cotton shirt and a cotton pullover, and shabby cotton trousers. Nothing else, apparently, except a towel over his shoulder. I myself was wearing flannel trousers and a woollen sweater over my shirt, and a tweed coat. I was by no means too hot in all these clothes.

'Aren't you cold out there?' I asked him.

'Cold?' He suddenly started to think of it, shivered miserably and burst out laughing. 'Yes, I am cold.'

'Who are you?'

'Pir *saiñ* sent me.'

'Sain,' with a nasalised 'n', is the Sindi equivalent of 'sahib' – a respectful form of address. This much Sindi I knew, at least.

'You can sit in the room, if you like,' I suggested. 'And what about your friend outside?'

'Are you not going to wash your hands and your face?' he asked me. 'It is Haidero outside. He has the hot water and the basin. He says the hot becomes cold. I have the soap.'

'And the towel, I see.'

'Yes. And the towel.'

'Tell Haidero to bring the basin in, then,' I said.

'Not in. Out. Because of the splashes.'

So I went out into the patio and washed. Haidero held the basin, and the small dark one held the soapdish and the towel, and a third man in the deep shadows just watched.

'And now your mouth,' the small one said.

I washed out my mouth to please them.

'And now,' he said, leading me back under the colonnade, 'tea. You would like that?'

'I would like that very much indeed.'

'And when you have had the tea, our Pir sain is coming to see you. He has told us to do everything for you. He is over there in his house,' he said, pointing. But my mind was taken by a golden orange floating in the night air, beyond the walls. He saw me looking at it and at once made a sort of bob to it and started gabbling softly – gabble-gabble-gabble Lal Shah Baz sain – and putting his two hands to his lips kissed them tenderly and waved them at the orange.

'Our Qalandar Lal Shah Baz,' he exclaimed. 'Our great and splendid Qalandar sain! Our blessed, our King of Kings, it is for him that the electric works, his the fine light to light our darkness! "I was there with Moosa", the little dark person intoned in the voice of one quoting the scriptures: "I was there with Ibrahim, I was there when Ishmael was to be the sacrifice."

'Ishmael?' I murmured doubtfully. 'Isaac?'

'"... when ISHMAEL was to be the sacrifice,"' he repeated firmly. 'I AM THE LIGHT!' – and his eyes shone and his gestures grew big as he faced himself towards the golden orange, his head held high and proud. Then suddenly he grew small again and said: 'You see?' – and led me back into the room, talking gaily.

A Cushion in the Skies

'You see? It is for our great Qalandar sain that the electric is working from its engine – to light his courts through the hours of darkness. This is the first time you have been here? Never before? You were not here before I was born? No? But you are here now,' he said consolingly, as he took me by a finger and directed me to the sofa, where he pressed me gently down. 'And tomorrow, *Insha' Allah*, I and Haidero will bring you to him. *Tch!*' He let go of me and hurried angrily towards the petrol-vapour lamp, which was gulping a bit behind me.

As he pumped at its malicious little heart and the flames once more hissed and exploded in fearful blinding whiteness, he jutted his chin towards the ceiling. 'You see the wirings? Here also in the otaq we have the electric, but a "bearing" is weak.'

He had used the English word, and I was nonplussed.

'Yes, a "bearing" is weak, they say: so the electric is unable to light our Qalandar sain and at the same time our otaq.'

The ceiling of the otaq is festooned with wires, as I now noticed. They hang about like a dusty creeper, lianas of electric wire, some of them crawling down the walls to what must have been switches, others looped up in the middle of the room as if in the past they had borne a flowering of electric bulbs.

'It works sometimes, in the otaq, this electric?' I inquired. It had rather an indisciplined look.

'Yes,' he said. 'No.'

'I see.'

'Because of the "bearing", of course. It cannot work *at night* in the otaq, since it lacks the energy when the great light before the *durgah-sharif* [the holy shrine] is working.' He was squatting on the carpet in front of me by now, and by shooting out one arm, making his fist and forefinger into a pistol and sighting along its barrel, he could draw a bead on Qalandar sain's nightlamp – though it was hidden from me at present by the arching of the colonnade.

The man who had held the basin came in. He is a little bigger than the small one. I felt it was time to make sure of their names, since it looked already as if I am to be linked with the two of them for so long as I am here. The third man was left anonymously outside.

'You are Haidero, aren't you?' I asked the larger one.

The small one answered for both. He is extremely unshy and informative.

'I am Akbar. And he Haidero.'

Haidero smiled and said: 'I am Haidero, and he Akbar.'

Haidero is two or three years older than Akbar, I should guess: and this might mean twenty or so. He is fairer and wears an almost laughably large moustache, a moustache far beyond his years and station, very luxuriantly grown, chocolate-coloured and spreading inches to each side of his upper lip. It is curious that this thing should give him a look not of the rogue male but of innocence, and youth – as if he had perhaps borrowed it in order to play at being bandits. His face is quite unremarkable, apart from this moustache, and I even wonder if I would recognise him if he were suddenly to unhook it and hide it behind his back.

'How old are you?' I asked Akbar, the small one.

'Sixteen,' he answered very promptly – and I think that although he meant it for the truth, he must have underestimated by a couple of years.

'Are you married?' I continued, as a sort of cross-check.

'Me? Or him?' Akbar asked. 'I, I am *not* married. But *he*, Haidero, is married and has two babies. Haven't you, Haidero, by the grace of God?'

Haidero said yes, he had. 'And how many babies have you?' he asked me.

'Eight,' I said, but with no sense of falsehood. They would certainly not believe me if I admitted that I was not even married: and if I were married it would be rather shameful and turned away from by God not to have had at least eight by this time. Nevertheless I must have felt a twinge of guilt because I added: 'Five of the little ones are no more.' That, of course, was so as not to seem overproud and blessed.

'As God wills,' they said. 'And girl-babies, how many?'

'None.' And this time, when after all I was speaking the exact truth, I was ashamed of myself.

'God be praised,' Haidero said.

'Have you been to Hyderabad?' Akbar asked me. His eyes were glistening, because Hyderabad is the Sindi city *par excellence* – or used to be some years ago and the myth continues: city of Love and Elegance; Paris, very nearly.

'Yes. But not for a long time.'

'The girls in Hyderabad *chakla*' – *chakla* means the whores' quarter – 'cost from rupees three to rupees thirty, forty, fifty!' Akbar waved his hands at these pinnacles of extravagance. 'For rupees fifty the girl is young and beautiful, the bed is spread with silk, there is tea and music (if you will pay more) and they will not knock upon the door and say "Be quick, O wretch! You think the world is yours?" But for rupees three the girl is less young, there is no tea or silk and the time is very very short and …'

'What do *you* know?' demanded Haidero, puffing out his property moustache. 'You have never been there. You have only seen the girls in Sehwan.'

Akbar's eyes lowered themselves sadly. 'Yes, it is true. I have never been anywhere but Sehwan.'

I tried to elevate the conversation. 'And Qalandar Lal Shah Baz sain? I would like to visit his shrine tonight, after Pir sain has been to see us.'

'Tomorrow we will take you. You will see! There is none to stand beside him and beside our Pir sain Gul Muhammad Shah!' And Akbar started bobbing and genuflecting again towards the orange suspended in the heavens.

I dare say this could have continued for ever, but Akbar's ears caught a sound that mine did not, and he quickly composed his strange little imp's face into an expression of humility. The door into the patio opened and a man came in.

* * *

It is easy enough to say what Pir Gul Muhammad Shah looks like. He is heavyish in build, and tall: he walks with a suspicion of a roll, as heavy men sometimes do. He is in his middle thirties, perhaps. He wears Sindi clothes, the ballooning pantaloons and a long shirt-like garment, but there is something Western about the cut of them. He makes a concession to the West in the way he dresses his hair, too: it is very thick, and blue-black, and is parted to one side. His moustache is blue-black and extremely neat, and his face is otherwise carefully shaven – a roundish face. He is the colour of ripening wheat. He is certainly rather handsome in his way, and he has a slow charm which, together with a wonderful sense of repose, make him a very agreeable person to be with. He is, of course, a Syed: a nobleman of Islam.

He came in alone – Akbar and Haidero scuttled out on his arrival – and I think I would have guessed who he was even if I had not been warned to expect him, because he has an air of majesty. I got up to greet him and to thank him for receiving a complete stranger into his house in this way. He smiled and took my hand, neither accepting my gratitude nor pooh-poohing it. Then he led me back to the sofa where he slumped himself down without more ado. So I sat down beside him.

Royalty, and of course saints, off-duty are seldom the easiest people to make conversation with, I imagine – unless you are supported by a sense of privilege and awe. In that case a sort of conversation might produce itself. Neither of you is likely to say anything very original or profound, perhaps, and the little platitudes from the lips of the great risk falling the flatter because you may judge them by inhuman standards. Pir sain made no kind of attempt to impress me – and indeed why should he? All he was concerned to do was to have me know that his house was my house for as long as I cared to remain his guest. This he did with such easy and natural good manners that I was able to think of him not as a saint off-duty, but as my host, and no more. There was no courtier present who could later say to me: 'Isn't it extraordinary how our Pir sain can throw off the cares of the throne and become like any one of us?'

'I have eaten already,' Pir sain was saying, in Urdu – for this was our common language. 'So you must forgive me if I don't feed with

A Cushion in the Skies

you. But I have told my people to look after you. Dinner will be coming soon. Are you tired? Do you think you will be happy and comfortable, here with us?'

I made some suitable reply, and we talked about various things, though I don't remember exactly what. In fact nothing of our conversation remains. It might have been deliberately designed to avoid overtaxing the strength and the imagination, either because conversation in otaqs is not intended for any such purpose, or because it was getting late and I was presumed to be tired and hungry – whereas Pir sain was tired and replete. After quite a long time he got up as abruptly as he had come in, and left me. I stood under the colonnade watching him go.

Pir sain's position is such that it can never be necessary for him to give thought to it – no build-up, no smiling *claque* to applaud at the right moments. He does not perform. He is by inheritance what he is, both nobleman and saint, and he need not take pains to remind you of it.

I turned back into the room. A brass tray laden with tea things sat on a chair behind one of the columns and Akbar, reappearing suddenly, precipitated himself upon it.

'Tea!' he exclaimed, and followed me into the room, bringing it. 'Now I go with Haidero to fetch the dinner.'

I took a sip of tea but decided that I didn't want it, with dinner almost on the way. So I tiptoed out into the empty patio and poured the contents of the cup into a drain. I was caught at this little deception by a stranger who came in at the door at that moment. He advanced on me and shook hands and steered me back to the sofa. He was large – larger than Pir sain – and a bit older and wrapped in a green cashmere shawl with an embroidered edge to it. He wore a little fur cap. His whole face was creased with good humour.

He announced who he was: 'I am Pir sain's – ' – but I can't remember the word for the relationship he bore to Pir sain, nor exactly what relationship it stood for. Paternal uncle's son, possibly. There was a distinct family resemblance. Then his eye was caught by a green tin of cigarettes on the sofa-table. 'Ah-h, Three Castles!'

43

he said. He took one and lit it, suddenly remembered me, took another, lit it for me and sat back blowing out a great column of smoke. 'We cannot get Three Castles in Sehwan. I'm going to take my dinner with you. I live in my own village, some miles from here. But I am here for a few days. What is your business?'

'I have come to visit Pir sain and the shrine of Qalandar Lal Shah Baz.'

'Good. And you like shooting?'

'No.'

'Some people don't,' he admitted, politely. 'What do you like, then?'

'I like ... food, and friends.' I was on the point of adding whisky, but didn't. 'And sleep. And, of course, Sindis.'

'Ah. You like Sindis,' he said with satisfaction.

I have been in Sind several times before, and though I do not know very much about the Sindi people, I am very much taken with what I have seen. Sindis are the easiest and most open of the Eastern peoples I have come across. They are less arrogant than the Pathans of the far north, less suspicious than the Punjabis who are their neighbours, and they do not seem to be tormented by any inhibitions. This is a great relief.

But a social problem must always exist between men of different race who are obliged to communicate in a language that belongs to neither. The nuances are lost. I don't pretend that Pir sain's paternal uncle's son (if that is the right relationship) and I – he Sindi, I English, and talking together in Urdu – would otherwise have given a glittering display of pyrotechnics, but we might have talked of subjects more improving than 'girls'. My companion seemed to have a deep knowledge of the subject, incidentally, and he discussed it in the nicest possible way. There was no leering, no hidden meaning. Everything was put squarely on the table, to the accompaniment of laughter and the smacking of lips. It would be nonsense for me to say that I did not greatly enjoy the conversation, even if it took us no further. It had to stop after dinner, anyhow, when a youth came in and joined us. He was one of Pir sain's sons.

A Cushion in the Skies

The time passed quite happily. Pir sain's relation hummed and sang to himself, and the boy drew patterns on the palm of his hand, first with my fountain-pen, and then with a red ballpoint pencil, and it was only after they left me that I knew how tired I was. I rolled myself in the razai, asked Akbar to extinguish the petrol-vapour lamp and prepared for sleep.

* * *

I awoke this morning with the memory of the drums still beating in my ears. I don't know what time it had started, but it was nearing midnight when my visitors had left me and I think I had been asleep for a while when the drums woke me. Once they had started they continued until they no longer had the power to keep me from sleep. Each passage was exactly like the last: it began with a succession of slow, resonant beats, equally spaced. I could hear the sharp strike of the stick, or the hand or whatever it was, at the same moment as the slightly flattened *boom* of the drum itself. The Aissaouwa in Morocco produce the same sort of effect, but on drums of much higher pitch as a rule. Boom ...... boom ...... boom – and after the third or fourth beat the intervals gradually shorten – boom ...... boom .... boom ... boom .. boom. boom – till it has become almost like a roll on giant side-drums, sustained for minutes and working up to a crescendo of sound that splits the air and then suddenly stops, leaving the night quivering. Then, while everything still quivers from the effect of it, they beat out three notes, equally spaced – boom ... boom ... boom.

Once, as I lay awake, a gong struck thrice. I got out of bed, intending to find my way to the drummers, but the patio door seemed to have been bolted from the outside. In any case I could not open it. I had to come back to bed again.

But when I awoke this morning the sun was aslant across my patio, making a triangle of brilliance on the four-square surfaces of the walls and terracing. I lay for a bit, watching the tip of this triangle slither slowly down the western wall, my ears open for the sound of movement outside. Nothing stirred at all. I wanted a pot of tea. I decided to wait till the sun reached the junction between the wall and pavement. For some reason this seemed to be a suitable moment for action, the moment when the complete west wall was lit. I got out of bed and went into the patio.

Akbar was squatting in the sun with his back against one of the columns. He jumped up and called to Haidero (behind another column) and then joined me.

'Now you are awake, sain?' – so I was an honorary 'sain' now. 'We didn't like to come in before because you were asleep. But now we will come in.'

I let them come in, but went back to bed, feeling that it would be easier not to take part in a conversation if I were lying with the razai drawn up to my nose. They sat on the floor and talked across the bed. I made an occasional grunt.

'What about tea?' I asked after a bit, remembering it.

With every sign of joy, a personal joy, Akbar sprang to his feet and hurried into the patio. He was back in a moment with the tea, which was no longer very hot but was welcome all the same. I eased myself into a sitting position. There is no bedhead to lean against, so I improvised with the bolster doubled up under one elbow. When Haidero saw that this attempt was not very successful he posted himself at the top of the bed and made a rest for me with his body: but this was not very successful either. Perhaps I am not yet sufficiently Pasha to accept such services. So after a polite interval I reverted to the bolster.

'The sofa?' Haidero suggested. 'Come, Akbar' – and they made as if to help me totter to it.

'I could walk that far,' I said, and got up.

Actually I walked out into the sunshine of the patio again, and they followed.

'The lavatory?' inquired Akbar with interest.

I might as well know where it was, anyway – so I nodded and we went in procession to the lavatory, which is immediately the other side of the patio from my room. It is very nice in its way: a little

A Cushion in the Skies

separate cottage, half of it open to the skies, with a row of bricks in pairs for squatting on. I went in and they waited outside, like the two recording angels that attend all Muslims – one to record the good actions, and the other to record the bad. These recording angels will not follow a man into the lavatory. I can't be sure whether this is because lavatories – like wells, and ruined houses, and the public baths – are the chosen abode of djinns, or because the bad djinns congregate in such places, knowing that the recording angels will not come in to interfere with them. But whatever the case, the angels wait outside, and mine were waiting for me with a jug and a basin and the soapdish when I reappeared. The third man who had stood watching unidentified in the shadows during the washing ritual last night, was there again now. At least I think it is the same man: he occupies the same sort of volume in space – fat and middle-sized. What I had not realised is that he is golden-pink in colour, with a stubbly white moustache and beard. He does not seem to speak at all.

I washed, did my teeth and went back to the sofa.

* * *

What I really wanted to do was to visit the *durgah* of Qalandar sain. I could see where it stood in the yellow morning sun – domes, tilework of gleaming shiny blues, turquoise and ultramarine: and I could see the great mast from which the orange had shone all night. But by day the orange is replaced by a little pennant to mark the presence of the saint. All this was some hundred yards distant, and a labyrinth of lesser buildings stood between me and it.

It could not be hard to find my way to the shrine alone, if I set off on the right foot. The problem was to set off alone. I like Akbar with his round African-baby's face (there can be little doubt that he is descended from African slaves, who were still being imported via Karachi until the end of the last century. They are called 'the Sidis' – the Sirs): I like Akbar, and I like Haidero, and I have no reason not to like the pink old man who hovers in silence. But I wanted to escape from them.

For their part they wanted to fetch a barber to shave me, or at least they wanted to help me shave: but they had to be content with watching me shave myself and with holding the mirror and shaving mug. They brought me my brushes and comb and would have oiled my hair if I had let them. It was obvious that my hair did not impress them, because Akbar remarked that he was happy to have been blessed with such a quantity of black wire spirals. Finally they brought me my breakfast and sat round me as I ate an egg and drank some tea – which Haidero would lean forward to stir from time to time, for fear that the sugar would maliciously reform itself into crystals, I suppose. These were kindly little services and I hesitated to beg them to leave me alone. Even the pink plump man, whose name I do not yet know, drew nearer as I finished my meal.

I had a final cup of tea and got up from the table. Then, plotting a plot, I took refuge in the lavatory.

'But you have only just ...' Akbar began as I left them, and Haidero said '*shush*'.

Though doubtless surrounded by djinns, I was free of my angels and by standing on the little brick footrests I could peer out into the patio through one of the ventilation holes under the roofed-in part of the lavatory. I could see Akbar munching a biscuit that I had not eaten myself. I saw him take the cork out of the bottle and smell my hair-oil. It did not please him. Haidero smelt it too and made a face. Their taste is for something sweeter and more loving than mine, perhaps. They did not offer a sniff to the plump pink man, incidentally, and I am still wondering what part he plays in this household. Finally Akbar picked up the tray and left the patio. Haidero lingered on: he had found my camera and was trying to open it: mercifully the opening mechanism is not at once apparent as such, and he failed. I saw him pass it over without comment to the pink man, who was aching to get his fingers onto it, but he failed too. This palled, and after a while they both got up and wandered vaguely out through the patio door. I could no longer see them, but I could hear their footsteps as they rounded the walls, and Akbar's voice greeting their arrival in what

A Cushion in the Skies

I took to be the cookhouse, from the clatter of dishes and pots and the sound of someone working bellows.

I stepped down from my perch and looked out into the patio. It was empty, of course. There was nobody in the main courtyard of Pir sain's house either – only goats tethered under the little trees in the middle, where some fodder had been thrown down for them. Pir sain's own colonnade from which light had streamed out through the screens when I arrived in the night, was still screened and silent. I stood wondering which of the three doors on the *durgah*-side of the courtyard would be the exit. I made my guess and was wrong. It proved to be a storehouse of some kind. The second choice of three necessarily stands a fifty-fifty chance of succeeding, however, and in fact succeeded: I found myself in a passage of whitewashed mud. A turn to the right a few steps, an alleyway too deep and narrow for the slanting sun to reach it. I followed the alley as it jinked and swerved, passing an old man who carried a bowl of lit charcoal. About fifty yards ahead of me the alley seemed to open up into a sort of piazza in the middle of which the mast rose up, held firm by a maypole arrangement of guy ropes and stays that descended in diagonals to whatever hold they could find. A ladder climbed dizzily to the summit, sixty, seventy feet up in the sunshine, and there was a crazy crow's nest just short of the top. The saint's flag fluttered.

* * *

Sitting in the shrine in the darkness of the middle-morning, alone yet surrounded by others who were sitting as I was, quiet, relaxed, unmoving, I don't know what passed through my mind, let alone how to explain my attitude towards the saint in his tomb. It was dark at the level of the tilework floor, and dark again in the high concavity of the dome above us, but vaguely light at some level in between where the pigeons circled in a veil of dust-flecks. Their wings cooed like doves.

The dome is hollow and empty and the walls are empty down to where my shoulders lay back against blue-patterned tiles. The floor is bare. In the middle is the tomb itself, heavy with ornament, but ornament so muddled and undisciplined that though the eye is led in bewilderment from one element to the next, from ostrich egg to witchball to the Christmas-tree tinsel that hangs like cobwebs from a canopy above, the mind remains disengaged and unmoving in the darkness. The canopy is supported on four worked-silver columns that draw into themselves nearly all the light there is, and the four columns are joined at the base by an incised-marble balustrade that reaches to about the level of a man's shins. I sat watching the people come slowly in or go out of the shrine, or else I turned my eyes upwards and watched the little stabbing movements of pigeons' feet seen through the material of the canopy as they strutted about on top of it.

The tomb is covered with a succession of brocaded tissues. A turban, yellowish-brown cloth, stands at the head of it. People suppose it to be the saint's own six-hundred-year-old turban rather than a symbol for it. It is like an immense unripe pomegranate, crowned with dying roses and leaves and a panache of feathers. At one end of the tomb there is an object hanging from the canopy: it is of natural stone, shaped rather like a heart but big as a big gourd. This is the talisman that Qalandar Lal Shah Baz was accustomed to wear round his neck on a cord.

The Qalandar was a wandering, solitary mendicant, alone in his search for God: in fact the term 'Qalandar' is reserved for exactly such a man, who sets out on the Way with no spiritual guide to help him. He came from Merwand in Persia, and his given name was Usman. The Sheikh Usman Merwandi. At some point in his career he sat for twelve months in an iron pot placed upon a fire in imitation of Ibrahim, they say (though I don't at all know what they are referring to here: Abraham never sat in a stewpot so far as I have heard) and as a result of all this cooking the great Qalandar's skin became red, and he took the name of Lal – red. Qalandar Lal Shah Baz – the Shah Baz being for the Falcon: the Red Falcon of Merwand. The falcon part of his name is because he was able, on occasions, to assume a winged form. He lived and died a celibate.

A Cushion in the Skies

Nobody seems to touch the actual tomb, which is hidden under its covers, and most people are too much awed to approach nearer than the silver columns and the balustrade that joins them. I saw a man standing against one of the columns, stroking it with the palms of his hands. Then he stroked his cheeks and finally kissed his palms, so that his lips should receive some part of the virtue that had come out of the columns. Another man, more daring, leant across the little balustrade and picked up the hem of a brocade cover and kissed it. But as a rule people squat at a more respectful distance and are content to look at the tomb, and some would just wander round and round it, round and round, their eyes fixed and their lips moving silently. After I had been sitting for a long time I got up and made two or three circuits of the tomb too, partly to ease the stiffness in my thighs and partly because it gave me the feeling that I was sharing this communal experience.

There are two dark objects in one corner of the shrine, like huge furled parasols: I went to touch them and an old man politely but firmly asked me not to do so.

'They are the battle banners of Hazrat Hosein and Hazrat Hassan,' he said.

It is from Hosein, son of Fatima and 'Ali, that stems the great line of Syeds – and from his brother Hassan stem the Sharifs of Mecca and of Morocco. People who believe that their holy battle-banners are preserved for ever in a corner of the Qalandar's shrine, say it is precisely because of their sanctity that they have survived the twelve hundred years and more since the brothers rode out to their last battles. Nearby is the Qalandar's staff, but it is all wound up in coloured cloths and is not visible.

I sat down beside the marble balustrade and rested my arm on it, being careful to fold my feet under me so as to avoid pointing the soles of them at anyone who might take such rudeness amiss. A man in rags came near and picked up something almost too small to be seen – a thread of cotton, I think: perhaps a thread that had fallen from someone's disintegrating rags. He put it into a bag with a drawstring mouth and moved on. He looked like a Pathan from the North-West Frontier of Pakistan, but I didn't speak to him. Another man came and squatted down beside me for a moment, mumbling verses and looking with half of his mind into my eyes. I suppose it was to determine what kind of creature I might be, with my whitish face and bare head, whereas everyone else had a creamish or brownish or blackish face, and a covering of some kind for his head in deference to the saint. But the man was no more than inquisitive, and when he had satisfied his curiosity he got up and moved away again. There was no reason for me to move or to make any sign of recognising what he was about.

Another man in rags, his fingers heavy with cat's-eye rings, passed near, searching for things on the floor and occasionally finding them. He picked up a little cocoon of dust – the sort of thing that forms itself when a draught blows into a room and rolls dust about like snowballs or cocoons. He had a cotton bag with a drawstring mouth like the previous man, and he put the cocoons into it. Then he continued on his search for more. He had left his bag near me, so I looked inside it. It was partly filled with dust and cotton threads, a bit of rag, and a leaf that must have stuck itself to someone's bare foot perhaps and later detached itself when the man came into the shrine to pray. Such things are evidently considered dirt of the sort that can be cleared away, and the shrine certainly has a well-tended look. The sort of dirt that you can do nothing about is the personal dirt of people who have no clean clothes and who, having come from a long distance to offer the saint their prayers, have had no chance since arrival to wash themselves further than the neck and elbows and ankles. There were a great many such people in the shrine this morning, I judged. For a moment I looked out through the doorway into the huge paved courtyard that fronts the shrine. A poet once called this courtyard 'the cushion in the skies'; but he added that it did not at all times resemble a cushion in the skies, for sometimes it was like the floor of the highest heavens. I cannot be sure which it was today. It was lit by a shattering whiteness. It blinded the eye with its whiteness, so I turned back to the refuge of the dark, with the other men and the pigeons. I think I may have dozed a little.

A Cushion in the Skies

Someone tapped me on the shoulder and said: 'Move from here. I must clean.' It was the man with the cat's-eye rings.

'Are you Pathan?' I asked him, moving up a little. A Pathan's accent in Urdu is shocking and quite unmistakable.

'I am *malang*.'

Malang is the word Pathans use where Persians would say dervish, or Eastern Muslims faqir: but all three terms mean the same thing – poor, with the material poverty of a man who has renounced the world. It pleased me to find a Pathan malang here. I didn't press him to admit that he was Pathan, however. I said instead, half-statement, half-question:

'There are many malangs here in Sehwan Sharif?'

'Many. Move that way ...' – and he swept a little where I had been sitting. Then he passed on, but his curiosity got the better of him and he came back, pretending to busy himself with a discoloration on the tiles. 'You speak Pashto?' he asked, scraping industriously at the mark.

Pashto is the Pathan language, and I do speak it: in fact we had been speaking just now in Pashto. So I said: 'Yes.'

He looked at me for a moment and then his eyes went flat again. 'I have work to do,' he said. 'You must move.'

So I went out.

Outside the shrine a group of men drained of all colour by the sunlight had gathered together with brooms and scrapers at the end of sticks and had begun to scrape and brush the pavement. They were all malangs, all Pathan dervishes, I was sure of it: ragged and hung with talismans, their feet bare, their heads covered with little decorated caps. One, however, wore nothing but a burlap sack with faded blue writing on it, a commercial trademark of some kind. He had cut a neck hole and two armholes, and his legs showed bare to the knees under it. A brand mark high on his right arm was like a vaccination that has 'taken' and festered a little. I took him to be a newcomer to the dervish brotherhood, a novice, only lately branded. Perhaps it was because this malang was so new to it that he had only one little talisman whereas most malangs have a collection of *tawiz* and talismans round their necks or pinned to their rags and to their caps. All this man had was a Royal Artillery cap-badge that he must have found somewhere. It had *ubique* written in the scroll under it and he had pinned it to the canvas skullcap he wore. I wanted to talk to him but he was too busy with his sweeping and I passed by.

Shah Jehan, the Moghul emperor, who built the Taj Mahal, is said to have built this shrine too, or part of it. It has a certain noble simplicity – a square façade and the dome rising beyond it, with the entrance to the tomb itself recessed and tiled in figured blue 'kashi' work. Apart from these variegated blue tiles, everything is white – the shrine and the court before it, the cushion in the skies, and the big, arched entrance building at the other end of the court: everything is plaster-white. The sky sails above it, infinitely blue. The effect is startling. The black-and-orange-striped tiger that used to live outside, but is now dead and has never been replaced, must have been even more startling. He was the Qalandar's, in much the same way as Mister Peacock is Mangho Pir's – or the lion was Saint Jerome's, for the matter of that.

In a sort of ambulatory at the far end of the courtyard I came across the drums: half a dozen huge kettledrums, and no doubt those I had heard in the night. They were of copper, with leather thongs to tighten the drumhead. I sat by the drums and watched the line of ragged men advancing down the court, scraping and sweeping in unison, their backs bent. Soon they would reach a row of ordinary town-beggars that had squatted just inside the entrance to the court where they could conveniently intercept the people as they came in. The beggars would have to move when the malangs got that far. I walked across to the arched and domed entrance building. Since I had come through it myself, earlier in the morning, a talisman-seller had laid out his stock under the dome. All manner of charms were there, to hang round the neck or fasten round the arm: little leather pouches or *cartouches* of metal in which you could fold a paper with a verse from the Holy Qoran written on it, or some other object with magical properties if you liked. And there were amulets of coloured wool that were very cheap. But the purpose

A Cushion in the Skies

of the thing standing beside the talisman display was less easy to determine. It was a big metal cauldron, only partly filled with water, with a small brass bowl lying drowned at the bottom of it. Drinking water? It seemed unlikely. Porous earthenware is more usual for a waterjug. A gong on a tripod stood alongside it. I puzzled my head a bit and then asked what it was.

'The clock, do you mean?' the talisman-seller asked.

'Clock?'

'Yes, the clock. Surely you can see ...' He reached down into the water and brought up the bowl and emptied it.

'But how ...?'

I think he took pleasure in demonstrating how. Most people like being in the position of the man who knows.

'You empty the little bowl and then float it upon the water in the big pot, and then it slowly fills – you see the small hole in it? It slowly fills, the little bowl, and when it is full and ready to sink, one quarter of the night has passed, and the man can then bang the gong.'

'And he bangs it thrice when the little bowl has filled and sunk thrice?' I asked, remembering the three gong beats in the night. 'Is that it?'

'Of course.'

'I see.'

'You wish to buy a *tawiz*?'

'No thank you.'

'I have the best *tawiz* in all Sehwan. You don't wish to buy this one?'

He held up a little leather pouch for me to see.

'No, thank you. I don't want any of them.' And then I changed my mind and started examining his stock more closely. 'Yes, I'll have this one.' It was a small blue stone, pierced like a bead. It looked as if it might be a turquoise, but at the price he named it manifestly was not. Blue is good against the evil eye, however, even if it is not turquoise.

'Have you a piece of wire and a pin?' I asked him.

He twisted a copper wire very neatly through the bead and attached it to a safety-pin. I thanked him and paid him what he had asked for it without argument. It was a very modest sum. Then I walked back into the courtyard.

The town-beggars were scrambling to their feet now because the malangs were practically upon them. One of the beggars was an oldish woman, translucent as wax and rather beautiful. She held out a thin, fine hand and I put something into it, and at this her neighbour snatched at the coin and the first woman defended it. But the attacker was bigger and stronger – a woman with a blue, carefully shaven chin – or possibly a man wearing a sari and ankle-rings, his long, braided hair down his back, though men don't have such well-developed breasts as a rule. Anyway, this strange creature now threw his arms – her arms? his? – threw its arms round the old woman and pretended to bite her ear, whereupon the half-bitten old woman dissolved into giggles and called out to me in mock panic:

'In the name of God give something also to — ' – but the Urdu pronoun does not reveal the sex any more certainly than a blue chin or breasts.

I gave something. I dare say that I stared.

'What are you staring at?' the creature asked me, laughing. Then it broke into a kind of dance, waggling itself and making skinny little arabesques in the air with its arms. It tried to make the old woman join in, but she wouldn't. She just stood there, safe with her coin now and giggling helplessly.

The malangs had finished their task and had started to straggle out under the archway, the man with the cat's-eye rings amongst them, but he barely responded when I spoke to him. So I waited a moment till the one with the unhealed brand mark came level with me.

'Here is something,' I said.

I handed him a coin and the little blue bead. He looked carefully at the bead and up at me again. Then he half smiled, but he did not say 'thank you'. I watched him follow the others out from the courtyard into the shadowy dark of the archway and out again beyond it into the piazza where the flagpole stood and the sun beat down once more as if it were eternal summer.

A narrow alleyway takes off from the piazza, in the axis of the shrine and the gatehouse, and the malangs wandered away down it. Buildings of sun-baked brick and stone rise on each side of it, to two and sometimes to three storeys. I walked down the alley at some distance behind the malangs, but anxious to keep them in sight and to discover where they were going. They did not go far. Not more than fifty yards ahead they turned into what seemed from my angle of vision to be unbroken masonry; they turned right, and disappeared; but a moment later the heads of one or two of them were again visible on what must certainly be a terrace, overlooking the alley, and when I reached the point where they had turned I found a stairway, rising between two buildings. Immediately beyond the stairway a little cotton bag with a drawstring mouth hung on a cord at about the level of my head. It turned moodily in the silence, first clockwise for a few revolutions, and then anti-clockwise, unspinning itself. I watched it, wondering if I should climb the stairs, and a voice floated down to me, a voice with a disagreeable timbre.

'In the name of Allah!'

I looked up and saw a terrible old man with matted hair on which he had perched a felt cap decorated with feathers and beads. He had a biggish cowrie shell wired to his right earlobe, heavy enough to have dragged the lobe down into an ellipse.

'Go on!' he ordered, in Urdu. 'Put some money in. Give, in the name of God!'

Another head peeped over the terrace – one of the other malangs. He had a small blue-enamel teapot in his hand, very chipped and battered. Beside him appeared yet another face, and I recognised this one. It was the man with the cat's-eye rings. I greeted him in Pashto and the old matted-hair monster (whom I had not seen on the cushion in the skies, incidentally) turned to his companion in surprise, and then back towards me. But there was nothing at all welcoming about his expression.

'Put a coin in the bag, in the name of Allah,' he ordered, in Pashto this time.

I ignored him and said to the others: 'May I come up?'

Nobody said anything.

'I would like to come up and talk,' I said.

They whispered together for a moment, and at the top of the stairway I could see the man in the burlap sack. He was wearing the blue-bead talisman that I had given him. He had pinned it onto his cap, below the Royal Artillery badge. I could see that he was nervous.

'I want to come up,' I told him.

'Come in peace,' he said nervously, looking back towards his companions on the terrace. So I went up.

The little door at the top of the stairs stood open, with a marble plinth, maybe nine inches high, pushed up against it as a doorstop. There were two little marble feet on the plinth, but someone had cut them off at the ankles. I passed by them, took off my shoes and stood just inside the door, looking round.

It was the malangs' sitting place, evidently: what they would call their *bhaithak*. If it were a bit tidier, and perhaps a bit cleaner too, it might have great charm. It is set back on the terrace above the alley, forming an approximate square: but an irregular section of it has been cut out to provide for the stairway by which I had come up, and there is a biggish recess in the back wall. The main alley thus fronts it, as I have described, and a smaller tributary alley passes under one side of it. In the middle is a tree, leafless and bleached like bones. It is quite small and dead because it has nothing but plaster and masonry to feed its roots on. Nevertheless it has an agreeable shape and is handy for hanging up teacups and an old saucepan. Apart from the dirt and squalor the *bhaithak* is very nice, but someone has made a very grave mistake with the recess in the back wall. It is obviously intended to be the focal point of the whole place, and it has been tiled in big, modern, glazed squares – pink, blue, black and a few bright yellow ones. The same tiling has been used to decorate the seat that goes round its three inside walls. It looks both hideous and uncomfortable.

A Cushion in the Skies

No one was sitting in the recess, however. They were all on the open terrace. The man with the cat's-eye rings seemed to be in charge of tea-making, helped by a scruffy younger malang who was blowing on the charcoal to encourage it to light itself and boil the little blue-enamel kettle of water. The old matted-hair monster sat glowering at me. There were others too, perhaps eight in all, variously dressed and decorated but with this in common, that they were all looking at me with something not very much short of hostility. Only the malang to whom I had given the bead seemed ready to welcome me, but perhaps he did not dare to do so because he was himself so new.

'I am the guest of your Pir Gul Muhammad Shah sain,' I said, bringing in my big guns.

'Why must this foreign person not give?' the old monster suddenly demanded, ignoring me. He was pulling up his cotton begging-bag by its string. He waved it at me. 'Give, in the name of Allah!'

I sat down beside the dead tree, pretending to be unconscious of the hostility. I thought I knew how to deal with Pathans – even Pathans of this sort. I had had plenty of practice in their own mountains, after all. I was actually in their home now; I was their guest in the formal sense, even if they didn't want me here. They were obliged by Pathan tradition to receive me as a guest, now that I had come in. This was no moment for begging. On the contrary, they should bestir themselves and offer me a cup of green tea, though God knows I didn't much like the look of the crockery hanging from the bony fingers of the tree.

I tried again: 'I am your Pir sain's guest at his otaq.'

They exchanged glances with each other but not with me.

Then one of them looked up and said: 'You have come to Sehwan Sharif to visit Nadir 'Ali?'

'Nadir 'Ali? Who is he?'

The monster looked at me as if I had offered them an affront. 'There is no one who does not know of Nadir 'Ali,' he said gruffly.

'Alas, I am an ignorant person from outside, and I have never ...'

'Nadir 'Ali is not here,' someone said.

Saints of Sind

'Is he in Sehwan?'

'He is in Sehwan, but he is not here. You can see that he is not here.'

'But I don't know Nadir 'Ali nor what he looks like so that I might see that he is not here.' I was annoyed. I had never met a group of Pathans so closed and discourteous.

Someone handed me a dirty-looking cup with tea in it. It must have been from an earlier brew, because the present kettle was still a long way from boiling, and my tea was tepid. I sat sipping it, waiting to see what would happen. Someone asleep in his rags with a bit of sacking pulled over his face awoke and looked out from his lair. He was very old, with a mad face and a cap covered with bright woollen bobbles. He was leaning against a row of waterpots, propped there in position. His eyes seemed to see nothing. I turned away from him. In an arcaded building of brick across the alley I could see a line of tombs, at the same level as the terrace we were sitting on. No one spoke at all, or even looked at me any more. Even the novice with the unhealed brand mark and my blue-bead talisman had lowered his eyes so as not to see me.

It is difficult to know how to behave if you don't understand the people you find yourself with, and I was obliged to admit that I didn't understand these. They were Pathans, all right: but they were very different from the tribal people I knew from the North-West Frontier, and very different from the Pathans you can see in the cities and villages 'down country'. Their faces and physique conformed to those of the various Pathan types, though they were scruffier and less well made than the normal. But they were apart, and hostile. I got the impression that they were sitting the situation out, in the knowledge that finally I must rise and leave them victorious. So I sat stubbornly on. Something would happen.

Something did happen – a little incident only, but enough to save my face. A group of men, a few women amongst them, appeared far down the alley walking in procession up towards the shrine. One of them carried something wrapped in a cloth. He was chanting. The others would wait for the breaks in his chant and interpolate a wild

A Cushion in the Skies

shout – 'mast qalandar! mast qalandar!' They looked respectable people. Their approach caused a stir amongst the malangs. The old monster with the matted hair and the cowrie-shell earring wriggled on his buttocks to the edge of the terrace. Having reached it he threw his moneybag out on its line and agitated it at the procession excitedly, shouting down as they came closer: 'In the name of Allah!'

The procession was too enclosed in its private world to hear him.

'Give!' the old monster shrieked. 'How shall we live if you do not remember Allah?'

The procession had passed by and given nothing.

The malang hauled in his moneybag and sat glowering again as I drank the tea. I finished it as quickly as I could so that I could go before the atmosphere of hostility, broken by the passage of the procession, should have time to reorganise itself. I reversed my cup and set it upside down on the saucer to prevent them from refilling it. I hardly think they were intending to do so, anyhow.

There seemed no point of contact between me and them. I didn't understand. I have met Pathan malangs so often in the past and have found myself in sympathy with them – but it has hitherto always been in their own country where they remained true to the Pathan traditions. Moreover in the past my contact has been with solitaries, like mendicant friars, 'qalandars' in fact, whether true or false. This was the first time that I had sat with a group of Pathan malangs of what seemed like a closed and self-sufficient order. They were expatriates who had wandered far from 'Pakhtunwali', the Pathan code. I didn't like them, and they didn't like me and I was ready to go, still knowing nothing of them or what they really stood for. I felt that I would rather learn nothing than be compelled to spend time on the rim of a circle that so positively excluded me. Now was the good moment for going: they had made the minimum, formal gesture required of a host – unwillingly, perhaps: but they had made it. I could go without dishonour. If I stayed on, I might find myself at a worse disadvantage.

I got up from beside the dead tree, thanked them formally and made towards the stairway. Nobody troubled to accompany me to the door and nobody spoke. As I went down the steps and out into the alley, however, I could hear one of them say: 'Nadir 'Ali will ask about him. What shall we say?' And another answered: 'There is nothing to say.' I think it was the old creature with the cowrie-earring.

* * *

Life goes on, in and around the otaq. I eat and sleep, and the drums still fill the night. I visit the shrine where I see the malangs, or some of them, and exchange the courtesies demanded by protocol, and nothing more. I go for walks with Akbar and Haidero, or with someone else who happens to have come in to take a look at Pir sain's guest. I have been to the edges of the little town and have stared out from a tomb that stands there in ruins, out over a riverbed that is now as dry and helpless as a sloughed snakeskin. Perhaps this was once some part of the Indus: but for a long time now the Indus has flowed well to the east of Sehwan, whose walls it licked in bygone days. I have been shown the public ladies of Sehwan, sitting at their doors and beckoning unhopefully, and I have resisted them because it is not at all difficult to resist such disastrous-looking ladies. I have returned, though only once, to the *bhaithak* with its bony tree and the malangs sitting in their rags around it. I felt it to be a duty to try again, though I was convinced that no good could come of it. I was right: no good came of it, and no particular harm, either. The malangs treated me this time with careful courtesy. It was almost as if they had put their matted heads together and had decided upon the course they should pursue if I visited them again. I have not even set eyes on the mythical Nadir 'Ali. The malangs remained exclusive. I have no means of telling what goes on under their skins, whether there is a stirring of an inner, secret life, or just an emptiness: but it has seemed to me that one of them, two possibly – the blue-bead and the cat's-eye rings – might be more friendly if only …

If only what? The 'what' may prove more complex than a mere absence of sympathy between us. I have been pondering over the

A Cushion in the Skies

little I know and talking to people and learning things. Some of the things I am told are not altogether new to me, but there are bits of detail here and there that are suggestive.

* * *

This is likely to be rather long and a bit peculiar in parts and uncheckable in others: and if, finally, I am mistaken in the conclusion I draw, then much of it is irrelevant. But I think I am right – unprovably, of course.

AD 711 is the great Sindi landmark and a good starting point. The Arab Conquest is to Sind what the Norman Conquest was to England, or the arrival of the Pilgrim Fathers was to America. Muhammad bin Qasim the Arab arrived with his invasion fleet and his catapults off the coast of Sind and cast anchor at a place called Debul. It did not take him long to subdue the Lower Indus Valley and to convert many of its inhabitants to Islam, and Sind has remained predominately Muslim ever since.

The exact site of Debul is still in dispute, but the identity of bin Qasim's principal companions-in-arms is a matter not so much for dispute as for a strange sort of live-and-let-live agreement. People like to link their personal heroes with that landmark of an event and, in the absence of records, no one denies that someone else's hero was present on the great day at Debul, provided his own hero is admitted too. Terence's orderly, for example, maintains that Ghazi Baba (by whose kind intervention his wife has recently given birth to a male child) was among the invaders. Perhaps he was. Others make the same claim for Syed Shah 'Ali Makhi, who was a figure of much deeper significance to Sind than Ghazi Baba.

The Syeds today must number many hundreds of thousands, but to be a Syed in AD 711, a bare thirty-one years after Hazrat Hosein, their progenitor, had been killed at the Battle of Kerbala, and only seventy-nine years after the Prophet Muhammad himself had died, was to share mystically noble blood with perhaps no more than a few scores of others.

Shah 'Ali Makhi was a Syed. He settled down at a place called Lakki in Sind and is there said to have married a Hindu girl-convert to Islam who bore him sons. He was prolific as a father, and his origins, coupled with a reputation for personal saintliness that grew as the years passed, made him an object of very special veneration amongst the Sindi converts. His influence spread and by the time he died the foundations of a spiritual empire in Sind had been laid deep and solid. The eighth century was still a good deal too early for the Muslim saints and saint-cults that in due course were to flower like orchids about the hardwood bole of Islam. God was still the Unapproachable, and no one thought of attempting to approach Him. But a Syed was already a Syed, and the people of Sind were backed by centuries of polytheistic tradition that Islam could obscure but never entirely obliterate. Syed Shah 'Ali Makhi's descendants became known as the Pirs of Lakki, or the Lakiari Pirs.

But perhaps after all Syed Shah 'Ali Makhi did not arrive in Sind with the Arab invasion: it could have been much later, and alone – in about AD 1260 in fact. Perhaps he came from Herat, in Afghanistan. Newcomers to Sindi affairs should not allow their judgement to be disturbed by this so-to-speak 'alternative truth': instead they should try to draw strength and comfort from the case of Mangho Pir and his Four Friends. The Four Friends seem to float above Time and History, and so does Syed Shah 'Ali Makhi. But the spiritual empire he bequeathed to his descendants the Lakiaris continues to this day, like the river Indus itself.

I shall now quote from an official government report of the late nineteenth century because it states a very apposite truth that I would find it embarrassing to present if it were a discovery of my own. The subject of the report was a branch of the Lakiaris that had broken away from the main line, and the writer was a Hindu civil servant who knew Sind. The details don't matter here, but the writer permits himself a generalisation that does matter. It concerns what comes about when a saint's descendants multiply to unmanageable numbers:

A Cushion in the Skies

'It soon became necessary' [wrote this Hindu civil servant] 'for some of his descendants to disperse, in order to get a separate spiritual foothold in the hearts of the people, and earn a living.'

... and earn a living. It was quite true. Hereditary saints were, and are, no less occupied with earning a living than ordinary mortals. Spiritual empires have their economic problems too. For the hereditary saints, a living depends upon this 'foothold in the hearts of the people', and a good solid foothold at that: and it is obvious that only one foot at a time could find a satisfactory hold in any one heart. The Lakiaris had a large 'empire', but they were not the only sainted family in Sind. They had their rivals. But they were one of the two biggest families in the business and their numbers were increasing whereas their spiritual revenues were not.

Once a year, in theory, a pir will make a royal, indeed a semi-divine progress, to collect the offerings that his subjects are waiting to cast at his feet. Even today communications in the interior of Sind are rudimentary: in bygone days they were non-existent. A progress was quite an affair. If a pir's empire were large, it could well take him the twelve months of the year to do his duty efficiently, shedding the light of his countenance right, left and centre, and collecting his tribute from each *murid* of each village – because he would naturally not wish to leave a single disciple unlit by his radiance. Consequently he would have little or no leisure in which to stay quietly at home, thanking God for His gifts and enjoying them. Sind, it must be remembered, is a country where leisure is almost as important as food. Of course each pir would appoint his *khalifas* – as his lieutenants are called – to do the rough work of administration, but revenue-collecting was something that the pir might somehow prefer to do for himself, or at least to supervise. A sensible plan would be to send away sons and nephews, all noble in the same sense as the 'sitter-on-the-throne' himself, to establish little peripheral pirships, preferably in territory altogether new to the family, but at worst in the family's outlying districts which were impossible or inconvenient for the pir to visit regularly himself. In this way not only would new hearts be reached but the number of noble stomachs to be satisfied at home would be reduced and at the same time these stomachs would be provided with means of filling themselves.

A great many pirships were founded in Sind as the centuries sailed by, and some of the most important were presided over by members of the Lakiari line. Kinship and community of interest, however, were not always enough to ensure love between the various pirs, for pirs have their human aspects too. They are capable of feeling the pangs of envy, for one thing. Across jungles of mimosa they would observe each other, these pirs and sub-pirs, through forests of tamarisk and acacia, over the great river Indus or the deserts to the south-east or the gravelly plains called '*pat*' that lay under the mountains to the north and west. There was really no room for so many saints and sometimes one of them would be obliged in self-preservation to dispose of a rival who threatened to gather to himself too many of the available disciples. And alongside these spiritual kingdoms there came and went a succession of temporal kinglets – Amirs, Mirs, Nawabs and such – the most recent outgoer being the British Raj. But the pirs, whether Lakiari or others, had a divinity that hedged them in much more securely than ever it hedged a king, and there the pirs remain, constants, in the great, wide, flat, lush or empty, saint-filled Sindi landscape.

There is no doubt at all that the landscape is filled with saints. They are of all kinds: original, miraculous saints who worked out their destinies along the Way and are dead these many years; there are the heirs to such sainthoods, whose jobs are more administrative, perhaps, than strictly spiritual or miracle working. There are the charlatans who go through the motions of sanctity and derive goodish revenues from it and, finally, there are other men who have not yet achieved sainthood but who struggle painstakingly towards it.

Here in Sehwan it was the 'King of Kings', the great Qalandar Lal Shah Baz 'who was noble, holy and knew the mysteries of God' and who died in the fourteenth century at the age of one hundred and twelve years, a celibate. He had no relative to whom his throne could be bequeathed. He did have a *khalifa*, nevertheless: a dervish and a celibate like himself. No one seems able to say definitely whether this *khalifa* was the nominated heir to the Qalandar nor, if he was, whether he actually occupied the throne: but at this, or a later period, an established pir very kindly took the throne under his protection and proceeded to sit on it himself as *gadi-nisshin*, saying furthermore that his son and his son's sons, Syeds all of them, would henceforth take to themselves the sacred duty of appointing successors to the Qalandar's original *khalifa*. Each succeeding *khalifa* thus appointed would be a true dervish and a celibate, and in this way the tradition that the Qalandar himself had established would continue for ever.

It is here that a little complication comes in – perhaps it is too small a matter to justify so elaborate a buildup, but I suspect that it is at the root of my failure with the Sehwan malangs, and it is therefore of significance to me personally.

Pir Gul Muhammad Shah Lakiari is, of course, the descendant of the pir who became *gadi-nisshin* at Sehwan. Nadir 'Ali, the King of the Beggars whom I have never seen, is the dervish *khalifa*, traditionally appointed by the pir. But which of these two is in the direct mystical descent – the pir who, unlike the great Qalandar is neither celibate nor, in the Qalandar's sense, dervish; or the King of the Beggars he appoints who is both of these things? A rivalry exists between them, a rivalry perhaps traditional. The pir's *murids* are ranged, naturally, behind their pir: but the dervishes themselves, that small band of celibates, initiates, are ranged behind the *khalifa*.

I take no sides, but the simple fact of being Pir sain's guest must automatically range me on his, and it must mean that a stone wall stands between me and the malangs.

* * *

This morning, for the third and last time, I visited the malangs in their *bhaithak* – principally because Terence is likely to question me closely about all this and I do not want him to charge me with having failed for want of pertinacity.

The malangs offered me tea, I drank it, we all sat in silence, crosslegged, looking down at our hands. On the far side of the alley the Kings of the Beggars lay silent in their line of tombs under the arcade. I slipped something into the old monster's moneybag and he pretended not even to notice and then, a final test, I asked if I might come to them in the night when they bang at the drums.

'Drums?' they asked in their turn, with eyes bland and vacant.

So later this morning, when I saw Pir sain, I told him that it was time for me to go, without explaining why. He took it much as he had taken my coming, or anybody's coming for that matter: as one of the mildly agreeable things that happen. People come – how nice: and the natural corollary to 'coming' is 'going': so people go – of course. There's no 'why' about it.

Akbar's reaction, when I told him in the evening, was rather different. I said I planned to catch the early morning train tomorrow.

'Where to?' he demanded.

'To Rohri – for Pir-jo-Goth.'

'But you said you would go to Pir-jo-Goth on Friday, and today is only Monday.'

I had said this. But I intended to telephone from Rohri to my host at Pir-jo-Goth, to ask if I might come two or three days ahead of time. So I now told Akbar that they were expecting me there as soon as possible. 'I must leave tomorrow.'

'*Insha' Allah*,' he said. Then he looked straight at me and said: 'Are you not happy here, sain?'

'I am very happy. But it is time to go.'

'You are not sick?' He was peering into my eyes and then at my face in general as if he were searching for a sign. 'Your colour has gone grey. I will call a masseur.'

I don't exactly know what he meant by this – about my colour having gone grey, I mean. It must be a greyness of the spirit that he was referring to, I think, because actually this bright winter sun and the hours I spend in it have made me progressively browner. But it is true that I feel greyish – because of those unwelcoming malangs. I don't regard my time here as wasted – very much the

A Cushion in the Skies

reverse: I have been very happy here. But it has not advanced me an inch nearer what I tell myself is my objective. I seriously doubted whether a masseur could be expected to help much with my 'greyness'; that was a different matter. Nevertheless I could see that I must agree to his trying, because it was like a final sacrifice to Akbar's determination to serve. So later this evening the masseur was brought to the otaq.

It was dark already. He stood under the colonnade outside my room, with his face lit only by a beam from Akbar's lantern. The lantern has become rather sooted up during the last day or two, and I couldn't see the man very well. He was immensely large, however: extensive, overstuffed, cushioned, spreading. He was wearing black *salwars* that ballooned about his legs. Fifteen yards of cloth, I reckoned. I have seen fuller *salwars* but only round the legs of the richest and most magnificent of Sindi landowners. Twenty yards is about the limit of grandness in such matters. The masseur's *salwars* fell short of the limit. He had a whitish shirt, slit up to waist level on each side so that a narrow panel of whiteness stretched down his front to where his knees would be. Folds of black *salwar* cloth billowed out through the side-slits. He also wore a very big turban that toppled about on his head. I took him to be a wrestler – what they call '*pahliwān*' – but an ageing, superannuated pahliwan. He had a moustache as big as Haidero's but of course he had a face big enough to support it and must have spent twenty years tending it. So there this masseur stood, solid as a Chesterfield sofa. He wasn't awaiting permission to come in. He was just holding a pose; making an entrance, as it were. It gave me a little time to get used to the idea of him.

A moment or two later he came into the room and undressed. It was then that he revealed himself in his full horror. He was even larger and more terrible than I had feared. He seemed to be completely naked, moreover – except for the moustache and turban. The minute bikini of a slip that he was wearing was hidden, at first glance, beneath the rolls of his stomach. But it was really too late to withdraw now – and Akbar looked so pleased with himself that I lacked the spirit to try.

A razai was spread out on the otaq floor and a sort of sheet over it and while Akbar superintended my own undressing, the masseur went into a set of violent gymnastics to show his quality – squatting and leaping, his arms swinging like dumbbells, his thighs bolsters, his moustache a terrible swooping bird of death, a raven, a rare black albatross. Meanwhile I was required to lie awaiting the sacrifice, with no defences except a little towel that I clung to as a prisoner will cling to the railings.

The masseur was sweating a bit already. He called for water to wash his hands and was led into the patio for this rite. He came back, drying his fingers on the tail of his turban. Akbar was carrying an electroplated cruet-stand like a Victorian coronet. It was filled with bottles.

'Now,' said the masseur, squatting down beside me.

I closed my eyes.

For anyone who has never offered his shrinking body to a Pakistani wrestler for massage, the ordeal is very alarming. The masseur himself is so much more bulky than men ought to be. If he should sit on you, you would be finished. But to begin with he doesn't sit on you: he squats alongside and makes a quick survey of his patient. He is a serious person. This sort of massage, which is called '*mālish*', is very serious. There is another sort called '*champi*' which could be done by marmosets or any other small creatures provided they had fingers and a light touch. *Champi* is quite different. It is sometimes genteel and sometimes not very genteel, but it is never serious or alarming. It is designed only to relax the patient and make him ready for sleep. It goes on for hours. But this was *mālish*.

The masseur leant over me, puffing a bit. He examined my chest. Akbar was with us, watching with some anxiety. What would the masseur think of me? Then the man took hold of my arm and waggled it. I let it go limp. He fingered my triceps and shook his head a little. Then my biceps and some muscles whose names I have never known. He took a foot, gave it a preliminary waggle and suddenly cracked my whole leg as if it had been a whip. It was quivering when he put it down again, but he seemed to be ready to start now.

'Jasmine,' he breathed, reaching for a bottle.

A Cushion in the Skies

'No,' Akbar said. 'Rose is better.' He grabbed for one of the other bottles in the cruet-stand and I butted in.

'Almond oil, please.'

'Almond?'

The masseur stood up, smoothed out the folds of his stomach and said: 'Very well. Almond.'

He removed a cork and sniffed at the contents of the bottle, smiled in a professional way as bears sometimes will in bear-pits and held the bottle momentarily under my nose. I sniffed and nodded, and he nodded too as he poured a little pool of oil into his palm.

'First, the leg,' he ordered.

I offered him a leg.

He accepted it, caught hold of it by the ankle with one hand and with the greatest gentleness laid my foot along the diagonal crease running from his groin to his hip joint. The crease might have been made for feet to rest in. Then, buttressed in this way by my leg, he leaned forward and started to pat the oil into my skin – *pat-pat-pat*. This done he closed his two hands round my ankle, gave it a few quick twists in contrary directions like fiery bracelets, took a deep breath and began.

The pain ... the pain was indescribable. His fingers had closed round my ankle so that there was no escape from them, and with a succession of terrible, leg-long thrusts he drove my flesh and my blood from the ankle to the knee to the thigh, released me, slapped me – *thwack!* – and began again. Oh tortured flesh! – again he did it, and again – within a minute my leg was mottled red and livid as the blood tore up it to the safety of my heart. The sweat of agony had broken out all over me. Akbar was sitting by, smiling contentedly.

'See?' he said.

Someone else had come in. The plump, pink man.

'Come in, Yusuf,' Akbar said to him – so at last I knew his name. 'Peter sain is having *mālish*. He was so grey and sad.'

Yusuf squatted down to watch. 'Look!' he said, suddenly concerned, and pointed at my navel. He stuck his thumb in it, but this displeased the masseur who slapped the hand away.

'Don't touch him,' the masseur ordered.

'But ... Oh well, all right.' Yusuf was vexed.

The other leg, a second agony to parallel the first: the arms, the neck, the agony – the whimpering, endless agony – the back: he battered at my vertebrae as if I had been a xylophone and then plucked at them and my nerves twanged like a zither. Then he thrust one elephantine leg between my shrinking two, and the other in some adroit and unexampled manner across the small of my back and suddenly he arched himself, a spring mattress that leaps and coils and uncoils with you in it shrieking for help – I shrieked aloud and almost came apart. The sweat poured off me, the sweat of pain past bearing, and from him the sweat of triumph and of duty done. In runnels it coursed down the folds of his fatness while Akbar and the plump, pink Yusuf sat there watching and murmuring: 'See? See?'

I closed my eyes again. I had no spirit left inside me, I was a finished person; a fowl – plucked, gutted, larded, ready for the spit.

'Are you feeling better yet?' Akbar asked, solicitously.

'When I was young,' Yusuf was saying as he ran a podgy finger over my thigh. 'When I was young' – he glanced at his finger, to see if it were bloodstained, possibly – 'everyone would look at me because I was so beautiful, and they would call me "soldier", or "Pathan" or "Pinkie" because of the fine pinkness of my skin. Not red, like that,' he explained, indicating me. 'I am pink. Look!'

'Yes, look, Peter sain,' Akbar said. 'He is not very pretty now because he has gone so old, but his pinkness remains like before.'

The plump Yusuf had pulled up his long white shirt and was displaying his stomach. Akbar helped him, and raised the shirt higher still.

'You see how pink? Like a soldier. They would all stare at me and make desirable remarks, and I would walk by. Even now, on the days when I shave ...' He passed a hand over the white scrubble of his beard, remembering.

'No,' Akbar told him firmly. 'Not any more. But the colour is still good. Pink, like a parrot.'

'Yes, very good,' I agreed out of politeness.

'And what do *you* think?' Yusuf inquired of the masseur.

But the masseur was regarding my stomach. 'I'm busy,' he said, deeply serious. 'I'm considering the sain's navel. I fear that ...'

'... and what did I say?' Yusuf demanded – because the masseur had now stuck a thumb into my navel, just as Yusuf himself had tried to do earlier.

'You see?' the masseur said to Akbar, ignoring Yusuf coldly.

His hand was a compass now, his thumb the pivot, and his fingers were describing an arc that passed just short of the left nipple, swung across the chest and missed the right nipple by a somewhat greater margin.

'No, it's not correct, is it?' Akbar admitted.

I was peering down the line of my breastbone, trying to see too. It wasn't quite right, as a matter of fact.

'The sain's navel is out of position,' the masseur explained. 'It's slipped.'

A slipped navel? I didn't at all like the idea of it. Moreover I didn't believe it. 'My tailor would tell you that I drop the left shoulder – a little,' I said. 'And that accounts for everything. It's not even an inch.'

'A tailor-master!' the masseur snorted derisively. 'What can a tailor-master know about slipped navels?'

'He's talking about navels – those things,' Akbar explained, in case I had missed the key word. Certainly I had not known the Urdu, let alone the Sindi, for navel before, but I knew it now. 'And is that why Peter sain's look has gone grey, Pahliwan sain?'

The masseur grunted. 'Yet I can correct it,' he announced.

Yusuf was talking again: 'My navel and my navel-tubes are perfectly in position in my pink stomach,' he said. 'You noticed, I expect. Look! I will show you again.' He lifted his shirt. 'Please hold my shirt for me, Akbar. Yes. That's right. Thank you. Now, with my thumb thus, and my fingers stretched thus, I can ... I can make a circle and ... the circle will pass exactly ... Look, the circle is passing almost exactly through ... *that* one, and ... Akbar, you do it for me. It is impossible to do it myself. Draw the circle with your little finger. Here! Give me your hand. Yes, and now with your thumb thus, and your little finger thus ...'

'Stop!' The masseur was very displeased and making noises to show it. 'Anyone can make the circle,' he said. 'But only those who are properly skilled can right the slipped navel. Please stop that business immediately. I need the help of all of you. Come now.'

They returned their attention dutifully to my stomach.

'Excuse me,' said the masseur.

He arranged the little towel in a more decent position and then stuck his thumb into my navel again. 'I must also consider some other measurements. The sain must lie perfectly still and not move.'

He described another tentative arc over my chest and then carried it round and downwards in a half-circle so that his little finger now hovered, vertically, a genteel helicopter, over my groin. Transfixed by my navel, I lay there motionless.

'Hm-m ...' he said.

Hm-m ... Leonardo da Vinci swam mistily into my mind – Leonardo, a drawing-board and the man he had pinned to it by his navel: the perfect centre of the perfect circle of which his arms and legs touched the perimeter like wheelspokes, or Saint Andrew. Hm-m ... another wretch pinned through the crutch, the perfect centre of the perfect square, head, feet and outstretched fingertips touching the four walls of their prison – the perfect man, responding on the pin to the canons of proportion. And another wretch pinned (by Marcus Vitruvius, if I remembered right) in an upended square, a diamond, equifaceted, the centre of the gem his crutch. A diamond, a square, a circle – but alas I must die because of my imperfections, a cabbage-white broken on an eccentric wheel and there is no escape ...

The masseur passed judgement. 'You are incorrect. You require a special treatment, and I will give it to you.'

He did so. I was past all caring what they did to me. I was a corpse under the hands of the washers, I was in the state of complete resignation that is required of a novice in a mystic confraternity, or as near to that state as ever I could reach. I was twisted and pummelled, knees were pressed into my back and my arms were

A Cushion in the Skies

taken and pulled from their sockets, I was banged and kneaded and manipulated, stretched, measured again, broken down again like a ragdoll, re-measured, and finally, in a muck-sweat, the masseur sat back on his hunkers to consider the result.

'Hm-m ...' he said. 'Hm-m.'

Then he leaned forward over me and put his ear to my navel. The others watched, awed and silent.

'He's listening,' Akbar said at last, breathlessly. 'What can he hear?'

'Hush.'

Lying as quiet as meat on a chopping-board I willed my navel to speak, to tell him what he longed to hear, but it wouldn't. Even the twitching in my limbs had ceased – I had passed into a new world of existence where neither sight nor sound, nor feeling, could follow me. I was aware only of almonds and of other people's awful flesh.

The masseur rose to his feet, towering up to the ceiling, filling the otaq with his presence.

'That will be sufficient for today,' he said, and shook his skin like a horse.

That will be sufficient for ever, for ever.

* * *

The early start, and the fact that the tonga promised for 6 a.m. was found at 6.30 a.m. in an alley near Pir sain's house tipped forlornly forward on its shafts with no horse in sight, did little to ease the aching of my body. But in due course a horse ambled into view with a man leading it.

'There's plenty of time,' Akbar said consolingly, though as a matter of fact he had no idea what time it was. He wanted to please, and was behaving as if two lifelong friends were parting for ever. Nobody else was stirring yet. We said our 'goodbyes' and I gave him a tip. He stood waving an old dishcloth at me as the tonga stumbled off down the alley.

I could see the station long before we reached it. There was no train alongside the solitary platform, which meant that it had not yet come, or had already gone, and there was no point in fussing about which it might be. Sehwan lay behind us, a little crumbling town with the Qalandar's flag flying over it.

I was surprised to find the newly branded malang on the platform. He had transferred his blue bead from his cap to the neck of his canvas shift: where it sat calmly protecting him from evil. He came up to me beaming with goodwill and we spoke for a moment or two. I had guessed right in supposing that he was friendly: he was now a changed person, separated from his fellow malangs. I asked where he was going.

'To Karachi,' he said – and from that moment things have not gone according to plan at all.

'But you're a malang at the shrine of Qalandar sain,' I said.

'Yes, but Nadir 'Ali has now sent me to Karachi, to the shrine of 'Abdullah Shah.'

The name rang no bell and I asked him who 'Abdullah Shah might be.

'He came with Muhammad bin Qasim, bringing Islam to the Sindi people,' he told me, and it pleased me to hear of yet another claimant to that distinction: Syed Shah 'Ali Makhi, Ghazi Baba, and now 'Abdullah Shah. 'I go to serve Nadir 'Ali's *khalifa* at the shrine of 'Abdullah Shah,' the malang explained.

'You mean that Nadir 'Ali has his *khalifa* there? In Karachi? How is that?'

'Did you not know that 'Abdullah Shah was *khalifa* in Karachi of our Qalandar Lal Shah Baz, then?'

'No, I didn't know that. But if that is so, then it means that Qalandar sain came also with Muhammad bin Qasim the Arab to Sind – or in any case at the same time: but there is the writing on the wall in the court at Sehwan, to tell the day of the Qalandar's birth and death and ...'

I stopped in the middle of the sentence, suddenly realising how pointless it was to struggle. In any case the malang was not listening, but was saying instead:

'Please give me the money for the ticket to Karachi.'

A Cushion in the Skies

I was not very pleased, because if he had intended to be friendly – and to exact something in return – he ought to have shown signs of it in Sehwan, when I was in need of his friendship. It was too late now. So I told him (what was the truth) that all established and self-respecting dervishes habitually travel without tickets. It was their prerogative, I said – though it wasn't really; nor was there a train to Karachi till the evening, and I told him that too.

'Oh yes,' he said. 'There is a train to Karachi now. Very soon now.'

'The train that comes now, comes *from* Karachi, and goes to Rohri,' I explained patiently. 'And I am going in it.'

'*Insha' Allah.*'

Nevertheless a signal was down on the Karachi track, which was puzzling. I called out to a coolie and asked him about it.

'The train to Karachi,' he said.

'Are you coming to Karachi?' the malang asked me.

I turned to the coolie again. 'What time does the train to Rohri come in, then? The morning train?'

'There is no morning train to Rohri.'

'But they *told* me …' I began, and then made a decision. 'If I come to Karachi,' I said, turning to the malang, 'will you take me to 'Abdullah Shah?'

'Yes.'

'Then I am coming to Karachi, *Insha' Allah.*'

And so I have come to Karachi instead of going to Rohri. I have two full days in hand before I must set out for Pir-jo-Goth, and this malang is at least friendly, or will sell his friendship. I have given him a small sum of money in token of good faith. But I have lost him, for the moment. It was my own fault. I got out of the train at Karachi Cantonment Station, because it is near where I would be staying, and in the flurry of arrival I did not remember to make sure that the malang got out too. He was secreted, ticketless, in a third-class compartment, and must have travelled on to the Karachi City Terminus. The whole situation is rather improbable.

3
Rock-A-Bye Baby

I SPENT A LAZY MORNING but went before luncheon to see Terence. He was surprised to find me back in Karachi so soon.

'I suppose you have a perfect right to change your plans, if you want to,' he admitted. 'You made them. You can unmake them. You're under no obligation to regard them as sacred. Incidentally *I* plan to take a good, brisk walk this evening, and that is a little bit sacred. Why not come too? You can tell me all about Sehwan as we go.'

'Have you ever heard of 'Abdullah Shah? A shrine, here in Karachi?'

'No,' he said.

There are only a limited number of 'walks' in the neighbourhood of Karachi. There is the beach at Clifton for those who enjoy their sand impregnated with mica that covers the skin like fish-scales and won't come off again except under a hard brush. Then there are some things referred to as 'The Heights' that rise a full hundred feet above the level of the sea and of the desert hinterland. Nothing grows on them, but from the vantage-point of their footage you can gaze some extra miles across the endless empty landscape. There are Manora and Sandspit and Hawke's Bay with their beaches and snapping turtles and other peoples' snapping dogs having tennis balls thrown for them. There is always the zoo – but Terence regards 'walking' as serious, and zoos as recreation. Anyhow he had already decided where he wanted to go that afternoon.

'Down the valley to the plain that is believed to lead to Las Bela.'

'Doesn't it, then?' I inquired.

'I think it probably does. It has wheeltracks on it, moreover.'

We stopped the car where the rough country begins and the road, to all appearances, ends.

'And now tell me all about Sehwan,' Terence said, bracing himself for his walk.

'Pir Sain was very kind and hospitable,' I said. 'And very nice.'

'Good. And the shrine?'

'Rather moving.'

'Good. And the dervishes?'

I felt that I must work up slowly to confession of failure. Perhaps it would after all prove less than complete failure: 'Abdullah Shah could be a success if I could only find the blue-bead malang again. After all I would not have even heard of 'Abdullah Shah if I had not gone to Sehwan. So I decided to play down the reluctant malangs till I was ready to deal with them.

'The Sehwan dervishes are all Pathans,' I said. 'Did you realise that?'

'Oh are they? That must have pleased you.'

'Yes. The malangs are all Pathans. The town-beggars are a mixed bag, of course, and there's a hermaphrodite amongst them.'

'Indeed? A hermaphrodite?' Terence commented with interest, stepping out resolutely through the dust and stones of the valley. Little dry hills enclosed us on both sides but opened up a mile or so farther on where already we could see the plain that was believed to lead to Las Bela.

'I can tell you a good deal about hermaphrodites,' Terence observed.

'I know several things about them too, as it happens,' I said promptly. Once Terence gets the bit between his teeth there's no holding him, and I knew that I must somehow keep control or I would never get the conversation back to the malangs and my particular problems. So I said: 'For example, I know that in Islam it is an abomination for them to wear silk, or jewels. I doubt whether that is common knowledge.'

He looked round at me sharply and his walking stick missed a beat. What I had meant, of course, was that I hoped it was not already known to Terence. It seemed as if I were in luck.

'How do you know that?' he demanded. 'And what are you translating by "an abomination"?'

Rock-A-Bye Baby

He likes things to be cut and dried. He appears to have read everything and to remember everything he has read, so I felt it to be doubly important for me to get my source and my facts straight. It took me a moment to do this. Then I said:

'From Imam Hosein el-Baghawi's compilation of the Traditions of the Prophet. The Hedaya. Captain Charles Hamilton's translation.' And I added the date of the translation, to suggest scholarship. '1791. The word Hamilton was translating was "*mekrouh*".'

'Hm-m ... I would have translated "*mekrouh*" by "not recommended", or something of the kind. "Abomination" is too strong. Surely *mekrouh* is nothing worse than "not recommended" – like shellfish in the Arabian desert, for instance. Shrimps are *mekrouh* for Muslims, according to the Traditions. Or ...' He was searching for another example, I suppose, and if I had not had a personal end in view I would have left him with the pleasure of finding one. As it was, and since I had a trump card to play in this game which he had started after all, I slapped it down in the momentary silence.

'Or for an equivocal hermaphrodite to appear naked before anyone – man *or* woman.'

Terence burst out laughing – as I had myself when I had learnt of this sad but perfectly logical ruling from the Hedaya. And perhaps I should here explain for the sake of those altogether unacquainted with Islam, that in the Muslim world actions are of four different kinds. You have *fard,* to cover actions that are obligatory – such as prayer five times a day, the fast during the month of Ramadan and so forth. Then you have the licit actions, called *jā'iz*: then *mekrouh,* actions of the type we were discussing with such competitive fervour, there in the valley north of Karachi – the not-recommended, but not-actually-forbidden actions, that is to say. And finally you have *harām,* or what is explicitly forbidden, such as eating the flesh of the pig.

Terence was delighted. 'I suppose that's Hamilton again. But what in the world could he have been translating this time? Hermaphrodite. All right: *khoonsa*, probably. But "equivocal" ...'

I don't think he expected me to be able to give the answer, but it happened that I could. My reading of the Hedaya had been very recent.

'*Khoonsa mushkil*', I declaimed, making the most of it.

'*Mushkil*. A problem. A difficult, problematic, or equivocal hermaphrodite!'

The mad phrase ricocheted about the hills, glorifying itself and Terence's voice and followed round by his laughter. 'An equivocal hermaphrodite!' A dog started barking angrily in a nearby village. Another answered it. The periphery of our world was filled with these sounds.

'Some years ago,' Terence resumed, quite calm now, and in complete control of his voice and of me and of the conversation, 'I had occasion to deal with an equivocal hermaphrodite. Officially. It was before the partition of India into India and Pakistan. In —' – and he named a little place in the old, undivided subcontinent. 'I was concerned with the group of Indian States round about.' He paused. 'I hardly suppose that either you, or your Captain Hamilton, ever had direct experience of hermaphrodites, had you?'

'No. At least I haven't. I can't speak for Hamilton.'

'No. It's rare. But I have had that privilege.'

The dogs were still barking, closer now. I looked away to the right, across Terence, and could see one working towards us. There was a second dog following behind the first, and I thought I could hear a third, on our left this time.

'So rare,' Terence went on, 'that in the English language, at least, we have no personal pronoun for anything that is not strictly male, and not strictly female and yet not an "it". Nevertheless I shall call it "it".' He turned irritably towards the barking, clicked his tongue and then turned back to me. I said nothing, recognising and accepting defeat. I might as well settle down to enjoying it.

'"It" was quite well connected, pretty as a picture and ten years old when its mother affianced it to a minor princeling. It had expectations of a little inheritance of its own, too. And it was prettier still at thirteen or so when it was finally taken in procession to its husband for the consummation of the marriage.' He broke off again, this time to pick up a stone. I did the same. 'A volley,' he directed, 'if they dare to come near.'

Rock-A-Bye Baby

'Yes. A volley.'

The dogs were already very near, as a matter of fact: three of them, big and starey-coated as hyenas, their lips curled back from their teeth. Terence waved his stick threateningly at them and showed them his stone. They halted for a moment at this, each with a foreleg flexed under it. As Terence began talking again and we continued our walk, the dogs came along behind, gradually shortening the distance between their teeth and our legs. They were growling, of course.

'Damn the dogs,' Terence said. 'Where was I?'

'Where it went in procession to its husband for the consummation of the marriage.'

'Oh yes. Well, later that night, the husband leapt out of bed with a shriek and ran in amongst the marriage guests shouting: "I've been tricked, I've been tricked! It's a boy!" Of course he hadn't been tricked – not in the proper sense of the word. The bride's mother was a good woman, and she had done everything in perfect faith, just as she had when she conceived it, carried it and brought it into the world. It was simply that it was *both* – a girl *and* a boy. But the husband felt he had grounds for his dissatisfaction and everybody else agreed with him, except the mother and the wretched bride itself. So the wedding was instantly called off. The pretty hermaphrodite ...'

'Take no notice of the dogs,' I broke in, 'even if they ...'

'... pretty hermaphrodite wept unrestrainedly and its mother ranted, and the neighbours all hissed together in corners for weeks over the shame of it. But the trouble had been made. Everybody throughout the countryside knew now. No wedding-bells for *it* – ever. Moreover, despite semi-noble birth and the prospects of an inheritance, its widowed mother was for the moment very poor indeed and consequently it was too. It could no longer hope for a husband (or for a wife, manifestly), nor could it find paid employment since no one seemed disposed to employ it: and, in addition, its relatives all started plotting in the most cruel manner to deprive it of its inheritance by one means or another. Its circumstances went from bad to worse. Within a few years its mother had died, and it had perforce taken to petty thieving.' Terence stopped at this point and turned to me. 'And this is where I come in.'

The dogs were still growling and following us. They were village watchdogs. I don't blame them for their failure to distinguish between two harmless wayfarers and potential robbers, but I do rather blame Terence. He insisted that we loose our volley of stones at them. This is worth doing only when you can be sure of your aim. We both missed. After all, it is easier to miss than to hit, and we both missed: and this so encouraged the dogs that they immediately came in on us, up to our very heels, snarling and snapping and salivating and menacing us, three of them, bristling and bigger than hyenas. We had only one hope.

'Pretend you don't mind at all,' I whispered with great urgency. 'You mustn't *in fact* mind at all, or they'll savage us.'

'But I *do* mind!'

'Exactly! So you've started to smell!'

I have often been menaced by village dogs and have tried to learn how to abstract myself. It's not insuperably difficult to do. It calls for faith, rather than courage – faith and a capacity to relax completely. Of course I can't always do it, or even often. It depends on the dog, to some extent – though that doesn't invalidate the principle. The best way to demonstrate to yourself the technique of it would be, I think, to be menaced by dogs when you are slightly drunk. When you are drunk you are not afraid: when you are not afraid your sweat glands don't excrete whatever it is that smells of fear, and dogs don't (in theory) attack. I cannot, naturally, promise that the system would work with trained police dogs, or even with mad dogs. Probably it wouldn't. But it does tend to work with the ordinary run of dogs who like their victims to be afraid, and on this particular afternoon I had managed to abstract myself admirably – until this moment when Terence's fear communicated itself to me and I started smelling too. But whatever the case, my whispers had a spectacular effect on Terence. They enraged him, not against the dogs, but against me.

'I do *not* smell!' he shouted furiously at me, and gave the ground a great beat with his stick. And from that instant it was true.

Slowly, and in the most magical way, the dogs withdrew. They snarled, shivered and withdrew.

'You see,' I murmured weakly.

'See? See what?' Terence gave the dogs a final frown and turned back on me. 'You've completely broken the thread of what I was saying.'

I said: 'I'm sorry. You were telling me how you came into the pretty hermaphrodite's life.'

'Ah yes.'

The valley opened out into the plain here. The village had been left behind. I imagine the dogs told each other that they had succeeded in scaring away the marauders, and we could now see them trotting back to their homes with disgusting self-importance. Ahead of us, haphazardly cut into the flat unending gravel of the plain, was a complex of wheeltracks, making off in various directions. Some of them looked quite new, but none seemed more certain of itself than the next. It was difficult to believe that anything could lie beyond, least of all Las Bela.

'Ah yes. It had been cast into jail for theft. Into the *men's* jail. And it hadn't been there for more than half an hour than it started complaining vociferously, protesting that it was a woman and should be instantly removed to the women's jail.' Terence changed the tone of his voice here, to suit a little interpellation: 'The fact is that in such cases male convicts are less fussy, from all accounts, than prospective bridegrooms. There is no doubt that it had reason to complain, and I was asked for a ruling as to its sex. So I called in the Residency surgeon. He examined it and made his report. What do you think he reported, Peter?'

'I can't think.'

'He reported to me in these words: "She is capable of being a woman." "But *is* she a woman?" I demanded of him. That was all I wanted to know, you see. And he repeated: "It is capable of being a woman," and declined to commit himself any further.'

'And was it capable of being a man?' I asked.

'That we shall never know exactly, I suppose. I directed that it serve its term in the women's jail – and to the best of my knowledge none of the lady-convicts ever complained at all (though this proves nothing conclusive, perhaps) – and I gave out that it was henceforth and for ever, legally, physiologically, spiritually, in every way till death do us part, a woman, God bless it! I did this from pure goodness of heart.'

He broke off and then said, in an entirely new voice: 'But why are you so interested in hermaphrodites, Peter? Have you changed your mind about the treatise? I thought it was to be the saints and the dervishes.'

'I haven't changed my mind and it wasn't a treatise. It was you who wanted to talk about hermaphrodites.'

'Not at all. It was you. Weren't you telling me a long, involved story about hermaphrodites at Sehwan?'

'It wasn't a long story, and there was only one – and I'm not even sure if it was a hermaphrodite after all. I only just remarked that there was somebody with breasts and a blue chin trying to bite an old lady's ear, there on the cushion in the skies.'

'You said no such thing! You must have gone dotty. This is the first I hear of a cushion in the skies. Why don't you get on with it and tell me what happened?'

* * *

So I told Terence about Sehwan and what had happened or, rather, what had not happened, between me and the malangs.

'I see,' Terence commented when I had finished. 'You haven't adduced much evidence of rivalry between the Lakiari *gadi-nisshins* and the succession of *khalifas* of the dervishes it is their duty to appoint.'

'No-o ... but I feel it exists. But what really matters to me is that for some reason the Sehwan malangs remained absolutely closed to me. It means starting all over again, somewhere else, you see. That's why I'm hoping that the people at 'Abdullah Sha's shrine, here in Karachi, may prove easier. Of course that blue-bead malang is only a newboy to the Way, but at least he is friendly and will help me a little, I think.'

Rock-A-Bye Baby

'You say that 'Abdullah Shah's shrine is connected with Sehwan?'
'It seems to be. But all I know about it is what Blue-bead told me – and Blue-bead talks with the tongue of the heart, which is not always a very accurate organ.'
'When did you say you were expected at Pir-jo-Goth?'
'Friday afternoon.'
'Then you haven't much time in hand for finding 'Abdullah Shah and Blue-bead, have you?'

* * *

Pir-jo-Goth was some three hundred miles from Karachi and fourteen or fifteen miles from the nearest convenient railhead. It would mean catching the early morning train from Karachi on the Friday.

On the Thursday, Terence rang me up in a very jubilant mood and asked me if I had yet found 'Abdullah Shah, but before I had even time to say 'no', he began laughing and said:

'Then you needn't bother your head any more, because *I* have found 'Abdullah Shah for you! He's fallen into my lap, and I make you a present of him.'

I was delighted and said so, adding: 'But why is it so funny?'

'Because 'Abdullah Shah is ...' He stopped dramatically. 'Who do you think?'

I detest guessing games. Animal, vegetable, mineral: I detest them, and said so.

'Because 'Abdullah Shah is Ghazi Baba!' Terence announced. 'You remember my orderly's wife's baby, of course. Well, I questioned my orderly, on the off-chance that he would at least be familiar with the names of Ghazi Baba's competitors in the Karachi area, and he was able to identify him at once. "Abdullah Shah?" he asked, "Abdullah Shah Ghazi? Why, he's our Ghazi Baba, of course." So there you are, Peter. You know where to find him.'

I was disappointed and I expect my voice showed it.

'Aren't you pleased, then?' Terence asked.

'Not very. I've been to Ghazi Baba's shrine – up to the approaches of it, anyway – and I don't like the look of it at all. I told you before I left Karachi.'

'I'm afraid you're not a very serious student, Peter. If I weren't busy this evening, I'd take you by the scruff of the neck and drag you to Ghazi Baba myself. It's Thursday. They have their weekly reunion at the shrine. My orderly tells me they do things in style at Ghazi Baba's – though it's less stylish since the police intervened.'

'You don't mean to say the police had to intervene?'

'My orderly says that the police didn't *have* to intervene, but that they *did* intervene. Ghazi Baba's congregation are rather sore about it. You'd better go and see for yourself.'

* * *

A young man, very neat and modern in his bush-shirt, tapped at my feet with the cane he held. He was sitting under a bamboo arch in a welter of discarded shoes. Behind him a stairway cut in the rock curved steeply up to Ghazi Baba's shrine. The scaffolding that had clung to the rockface at the time of my previous visit was still there, but it looked as if paint-pots were starting to oust the cement-sacks now. The renovations were coming along. I took my shoes off.

It was under the bamboo arch that I had come across the dervish with a cockatoo in his hair and had turned tail – not at sight of him, but at sight of what they were doing to the shrine. I had seen the tree perched on a ledge forty feet above us, just short of the entrance to the shrine, and had been able from that distance to identify some of the objects festooned about its branches. This time I climbed the steps, and stopped at the ledge to examine the tree at close quarters. Pennants of cloth on poles had been stuck into the crest of the tree, like banderillas, and there were bits of rag tied to the twigs all over the place. There were a good many electric bulbs tied on too, but they were not even wired for lighting. They had a different significance, perhaps, a sympathetic-magical significance. Were they symbols for the womb, with life waiting to stir inside? Fertility. All over the tree were dolls' cradles, ex-voto offerings, dozens of them, some doll-size, some big enough for very small babies: but the biggest were too big for the dead tree to carry and had been set up under it, on the ledge. The sun was on its way down over the Arabian sea so that the eastern façade of the shrine, before which I now stood, was in shadow. Not so Clifton, a couple of hundred yards inland from the shrine. Clifton was floodlit by the westering sun.

Sir Richard Burton – who knew Mister Peacock and who wrote about Sind – knew Clifton too, and described it: '... a barren, rugged rock, rising a few feet above the level of a wretched desert plain, close to the sea, and supporting some poor attempts at human habitations ...'

That was in the eighteen-fifties. In 1890, one Alexander Baillie published a book called *Kurrachee*:

'Winter at Clifton!' [he exclaimed] 'The very idea makes one shudder! On a November afternoon you may drive out under a hot sun, to find the houses tenantless, the place absolutely empty: not a soul visible, not even a dog to bark, though I believe there is a resident *pir* who lives in a cave at the foot of the cliff.' Today Clifton supports a great many rich attempts at human habitations and Burton would scarcely recognise it. The barren rock he noted is now awash with filigree-concrete villas, each more dismaying than the last. But the shrill, thick, vaporous, mica-laden wind that roars in from the beaches casts a merciful haze over the details.

I turned and confronted Ghazi Baba's shrine. It was obviously to be embellished in the full tradition of Clifton modernismus. Having turned, I lacked the heart to look too closely. I went inside.

Ghazi Baba seems to have become very prosperous since the time when Alexander Baillie believed there might be a resident pir; living in a cave at the foot of the cliff. Everything is very different now.

Shrines in Sind do not vary much in their layout. The tomb itself will occupy the centre, with space left free all round, and a dome above it. It is the atmosphere that varies. Sehwan-Sharif had been dark and peaceful. Ghazi Baba's reconditioned shrine, perched on its tumulus, vibrated with the winds that came screaming through on their way to tease the inhabitants of Clifton.

As soon as I came in I recognised the dervish sitting beside the tomb – because of the cockatoo. But as the man was inside the shrine today, he wore a covering for his head, and the cockatoo sat on top of that. There were a dozen or so other people in the shrine as well, respectable looking and good tempered. The dervish gave no sign of recognising me. I went up to him.

'Peace be upon you,' I said. 'I am looking for a malang with a blue bead.'

I had spoken in Urdu, and from the man's accent when he replied I realised that he was a Pathan. 'What is his name?' he asked.

I changed to Pashto: 'I don't know his name, O malang, but he is from Sehwan-Sharif and he came two days ago. He has a blue bead.'

'Khaista Khan …?' he asked tentatively – and then broke into the ritual of Pashto greetings that had been omitted because we had started off in Urdu. 'Khaista Khan came two days ago from Sehwan,' the malang resumed.

'Perhaps that is his name. Is he here?'

'He is below. In the *langar*.' *Langar* means kitchens. 'Who are you?'

'I am English.'

'Many come to Ghazi Baba – of all nations,' he commented in rather a showing-off sort of way, making a gesture with his arm that woke the cockatoo who suddenly stretched its wings, screamed, and raised a yellow crest. 'You have seen Pir sahib?'

'Not yet.'

'He is praying.'

'What is his name?'

'Syed Maidan 'Ali Shah.'

'He is *khalifa*?'

'He is *gadi-nisshin*.' The malang nodded as he said it, put up his hand and caught the cockatoo round its neck, lifting it down to his lap, where it sat quite contentedly. It had lowered its crest now, and was flattening its body out on the man's knee, making little kissing noises.

'Sit with me and wait,' the malang said, fondling the bird.

This was more hopeful than Sehwan, anyhow.

Rock-A-Bye Baby

So, if Blue-bead were to believed, the *gadi-nisshin* at Ghazi Baba's shrine was nominated by the *Khalifa* of the dervishes at Sehwan: nominated, that is to say, as successor on the throne of an earlier *khalifa* who had become a saint in his own right.

I sat down beside the malang. We spoke a little, though not much. After a while I held out my hand to the cockatoo and it turned its head upside down – to observe me better, perhaps, or else to express an emotion I could not identify. The malang put it into my hands and it stood there, suddenly shivering, so I gave it back to him, and as I did so I became aware of somebody standing behind me. I looked round.

'Pir sahib,' the malang said, without moving or even looking up.

A man was standing in an archway, a modern concrete archway that framed a staircase leading upwards, presumably to the roof. In his exotic way he had a face of extraordinary strength and beauty: a good nose, eyes that lay slantingly in their sockets – tartar eyes, mongol eyes: a heavyish moustache. He was not a large man, but he gave an impression of size – and of authority. He was wearing a cap called '*tōp*', which is a 'cloche' with a rectangular section cut out to frame the face. It was lined with fur. In his right ear was a crystal drop, tear-shaped and mounted in a little silver ring that passed through his earlobe. He had intelligence and a good deal of humour in his expression and when he had given me time to take stock of him he came forward.

'You have come to visit the new shrine?' he asked in a social voice – but a good rich voice for all that. 'Beautiful, isn't it? You speak Pashto: I heard you just now. We will speak in Pashto. Let me show you round. Of course it isn't finished yet, but already you can get an idea. Within a month or so, it will be complete.'

'Are you Pathan, then, Pir sahib?'

He smiled and said: 'I am from Sehwan-Sharif. You have been? Yes? Then you know Nadir 'Ali – you have come to me from Nadir 'Ali. I see. I am happy to welcome you.'

He was leading me round the shrine, a pace or two ahead of me, so it was possible to avoid comment on this, even if silence can also be an untruth. He seemed anxious to show me not the tomb itself, but the new elements that were now being added – the dome, the windowed ambulatory, the new encaustic tiles that lay in livid stacks awaiting their turn. The tomb had a screen of varnished woodwork round it, and some glazed panels with scenes painted on them, as in downtown Karachi cafés. I turned away from them. It was all rather awful – but the view from the open, still-frameless window embrasures was like the view across infinity, sand and sea, waves and rolling dunes, with the sun striking shadows from the eastern face of whatever had form enough to cast them. The light streamed in from the sun and up from the infinities of space of this sunlit lunar landscape, filling the undersides of everything – the dome, our eye-sockets.

'The court,' announced Pir sahib, at one of the embrasures. He waved a hand majestically over the buildings huddled below to seaward of the tumulus on which the shrine is built. 'We will perhaps rebuild that too, when more money comes, if God wishes. You see the guestrooms round the court? And the kitchens, the *langar*, in the corner? And the court itself – you see the praying place? Many people come – from all nations.'

I could see it all, laid out below us. And looking northwards, less than half a mile away, I could also see a pier in ordure-coloured stone. It stood disconsolately on the beach, without even so much as an inch of water to paddle in. I knew that poor deserted pier of old, and how the ocean has scorned it and drawn back its skirts in order to humiliate it. I turned to Pir sahib again.

'Is a malang called Khaista Khan with you?' I asked.

Pir sahib was not really listening. 'Come,' he said. 'What? Khaista Khan, you said? Yes, yes, I think so. Someone came ... Come! I will show you my room, where I pray and sleep. Look! This is where I pray and sleep.'

The room had a mattress and two or three ancient copies of the Qoran disposed on little reading desks.

'And you have not seen the cave, and the sacred spring,' Pir sahib went on. 'Come, I will show you.'

Rock-A-Bye Baby

He took me by the arm and I had the ridiculous feeling that I was being conducted round at a housewarming party. In a moment I might be asked to admire the wedding presents – an épergne, or a fish-slice, or even a canteen of superior electroplate.

'Are you married?' I asked, before I could stop myself, and he said 'no', without any particular emphasis.

It was unthinkable that a Pathan of Maidan 'Ali's age – thirty? forty? – should be unmarried in the ordinary way. The link with the celibates of Sehwan was tightening. We were at the top of the rock steps now, at the landward entrance to the shrine and Maidan 'Ali was inviting me to come down.

'That is the place for my tomb – beside the others who came before me,' he said as we passed a row of graves on a narrow rock ledge, near the petrified tree. He was just mentioning it, in passing, as it were.

'You are nominated from Sehwan?' I asked.

'Yes, of course. I and the line before me are nominated from Sehwan. The *Khalifa*.'

So that was it. The successors to the *Khalifa* of the Qalandar in Karachi were nominated by the *Khalifa* of the Sehwan dervishes, not by the Lakiari Pir of Sehwan.

At the bottom of the steps I put my shoes on again and gave a coin to the young man who had been guarding them. Two men came up and took Maidan 'Ali's hand, each in his turn laying his left cheek to it, his right cheek, his lips. We walked on round the base of the tumulus, past a ragged-looking garden from which a big, brash, copper-coloured girl stared at us. She had fine eyes and her breasts stood out under her draperies like little canteloupe melons. One of the men with us looked back at her, and I did too. She was still standing there.

Fifty yards farther on we had reached the eastern face of the tumulus, and a gate, through which we now passed into the courtyard we had looked down upon from the shrine. The court was empty, and Pir sahib led me into a smaller court, right under the lee of the rock. It held one or two stunted trees, and a good many animals – goats, and a gazelle with a little collar and chain. There were birds of various kinds, too: the pigeons were free to fly as they pleased, but most of the others, including an Australian pink and grey parrot, a Chikor and a Persian Black Partridge, were caged.

'Gifts,' observed Maidan 'Ali. 'The cockatoo you saw in the shrine was the gift of a *havildar* in the Baluch Regiment one hundred years ago. These' – he indicated them with a sweep of the hand – 'are the gifts of other persons. Please come this way. Yes. You should take off your shoes here.'

We shuffled off our shoes and I followed him into the cave.

It is obviously a place of great antiquity. Though facing west, the setting sun could not enter it because of the little buildings at its mouth, but it was lit by two or three low-powered bulbs, hooked here and there. A few yards inside the entrance to the cave some steps led down to a minute tomb-like grotto, over which a dome had been erected – and it was in this little cave-within-a-cave that 'Abdullah Shah Ghazi had passed his days, they told me.

'Qalandar Lal Shah Baz came here,' someone said, but I forbore to ask at what epoch.

An old malang sat at the entrance to the grotto, and another beside a sort of towel-horse nearby, laden with tin mugs. Beyond all this the cave floor dropped away, first in a gentle slope and then more sharply, in steps cut into the rock.

'And here we have the sacred spring,' said Maidan 'Ali. I stood looking down towards it as he clapped his hands and a malang came up.

'Take our visitor down to the spring and give him to drink,' he ordered, and then turned back to me. 'I will see you again very soon. I must leave you now. There are arrangements to be made for the evening.' After a moment's silence he said – rather pointedly, I thought, as if to underline the honour: 'Visitors are not really permitted to go right down to the side of the spring. They have to stay behind the barrier. But *you* may go. Go with my malang.'

Pir sahib left us.

'Come,' the malang said, unhitching a crazy old bit of wire that seemed to serve as a barrier.

At the bottom of the steps a pool lay flat and blue in the yellow light, and I followed the malang down to it. As I got near I could see bubbles and movement on the sandy floor of it, and the glint of little coins.

'Shall I throw one in?' I asked.

'Only the people who are not permitted to approach the spring need throw their coins,' the man said. 'They cannot believe that it is water, so quiet it lies there: and they believe only when they see the splash.' He looked pensively at the coin I held. 'You may throw if you like. Or otherwise you may ... It is just as you please. I will accept the coin, if you prefer.'

I gave him the coin and he pocketed it. Then he drew a mug of spring water and I sipped it.

'It cures all sicknesses,' he said.

Typhoid too? I wondered about this as I sipped. I had taken the precaution of having a typhoid talisman injected into my arm before coming to the East. The cold, blue water bubbled up quietly and eternally from the sands of this desert seaboard.

The sun was setting when I came out of the cave. Pir sahib was busy. I saw him as I passed on my way out of the cave: he was sitting on a bed, with a couple of serious-looking men before him. He had a bottle of something and, uncorking it, blew softly into it. The men had little talismans in their hands and I thought I saw some red wool. But I passed on, thinking that I should not disturb the séance.

I looked into the main court and saw that people had started to arrive, presumably for the soirée, and that the daïs in the centre was now crowded with men in the attitudes of prayer. They faced Mecca, but instead of the *mihrab* – the customary recess in the walls of mosques or praying places that points to Mecca – there was an empty throne. It was a four-poster bed, perhaps, rather than a throne in the ordinary sense: a comfortable, big bed, with cushions and coverings and a decorated panel on the wall behind it. I went back into the inner court to rejoin Pir sahib, if he were free again now: but he had disappeared and I was told that he was praying, in his private rooms. So I sat in the inner court for a while, alone with the birds and beasts, and then remembered that I had not yet seen Blue-bead, so I asked for him and was shortly taken to him in the kitchens. I sat and drank tea with him and his companions, all Pathans. They were very friendly, but with the exception of Blue-bead they had the appearance of men who worked in the docks or else in ships, and not at all of dervishes, malangs. After a bit my mind was distracted from our conversations by increased noise in the main court, so I looked out again to see what was happening.

More and more people were coming in through the gate. They looked respectable; artisans for the most part, perhaps. Everybody was congregating near the throne, where they squatted down to talk and wait. I joined them. We did not wait long. Blue-bead came into the court to look for me and said that Pir sahib was coming now. A neon striplight flickered above the throne, hesitated, steadied itself, and broke into its silver brilliance, turning fair skins green with brown blotches and dark skins purple with still darker purple blotches. I cannot say that it was very becoming to any of us. Then Pir sahib made his entrance.

He had dressed himself up a bit for the soirée – a gold-brocaded 'top' on his head, fur-lined: a sort of kaftan, and a good many rings set with semi-precious stones – cornelians, agates and the like. He advanced across the court, bowing to left and right, much as the chairman of a municipal fête committee might bow and wave on his way to preside at the function. He greeted me, amongst others, and beckoned me forward to a hard little seat alongside the throne. I had not given much thought to the throne until this minute, but now it suddenly came in upon me that if Pir sahib had taken his seat on it a few minutes earlier, it would have been to him, to the 'sitter-on-the-throne' that the faithful addressed their prayers. But the throne had been empty during the prayers: and though Pir sahib had prayed, he had not joined the men on the daïs to do so.

Whatever the mystic implications, it was clear that Pir sahib alone would sit upon the throne. Later on, it is true, a child was lugged up to sit beside him, but that was different. Three or four malangs – from the cave, rather than from the kitchens – had shambled in and disposed themselves at his feet – but in this highly respectable gathering of citizens, the malangs had the appearance of clowns, of mummers in fancy-dress rags. Someone with a small portable harmonium had come in too. We all settled down to a jolly evening.

It *was* rather jolly, I suppose. Everyone looked so happy. The atmosphere had a benign jauntiness about it, and at the same time there was the air of a jumble sale, in a rectory garden perhaps, with all those malangs like bargains on a remnant stall, to be picked over and paid too much for in a good cause. Would there be trestle tables in the background somewhere, with their load of lemonade and buns?

The man with the harmonium played upon it. He squatted in front of it and worked the bellows with his left hand, picking out a squeaky little tune with his right. Then he sang a bit, in a wheezy, tortured voice which caused the tendons to knot themselves in his throat, his eyes screwed up in agony – but of course it was only a very little sound that he produced and a very little agony, and if we talked loud enough we almost ceased to notice it, and in fact we talked all through his songs and smoked cigarettes. Mercifully Pir sahib had not yet thought of installing a microphone system in his courts, for a microphone can fill the world with what is, by nature, no more than a wheezing.

The singer sang on to the strains of his harmonium. We must have numbered a hundred and fifty at least in the congregation, but there wasn't a girl in the place that I could see. I asked my neighbour about it. A shrine of fertility, after all ...

'Those police,' he whispered in a shuttered voice. 'The ladies are scared to come any more.' His English was very fluent.

'But why?'

'Those police made such a fuss. It was a great shame on the police.'

The singer sang on, inexhaustible.

It was warm-hearted and friendly. I was not excluded – indeed I was made more than welcome. The neon lights flared out over us, over our faces green or purple.

My neighbour said: 'This time he is singing a very wonderful song about mysticals.'

We all beamed at each other and made more conversation. A malang in a travesty of a sergeant's uniform, with a bouquet of bougainvillea blossom stuck in his solar-topee, did a burlesque of a parade ground for us, using a broom for rifle. Everyone laughed, myself amongst them.

'I see that you are much enjoying,' my neighbour said.

'Yes,' I said politely.

'And you are much interested in mysticals, isn't it? In God and the secrets, yes?' I don't know how I could have replied to this question, and fortunately he did not require me to, for suddenly he took a pencil out of his pocket and started twiddling it. 'You see this pencil, yes? *You* say it is a pencil: but *I* say you are unable to perceive the truth in this pencil, that it is filled with the attributes of God! You see the difference? The door is closed to you, sir.' He sat there nodding. 'But it is open to me.'

I cannot doubt that he was sincere, that they were all sincere; but he, and they, and the place itself lay beyond the limits of my sympathy – it was wrong for me, and I felt that I must leave as quickly as I could.

'You must come again next Thursday,' my neighbour was saying.

'Alas, I shall not be here next Thursday. I leave tomorrow.'

'Tomorrow?'

'Yes. Very early. In fact I must slip away now, or I shall oversleep and miss my train. It's getting late.'

'Ah, but it's a pity to go so soon, when everyone is so much enjoying!'

I was firm and slipped away – but I stopped for a moment at the gateway to look back and wonder if this was what I had understood by the esoteric mysteries. Was it all as easy as this for some people, then?

4
Pagāro – I

IT IS A DEAD PLACE, altogether dead. Some of the people have remained, though there is little enough to remain for now, God knows. You might expect those who are still here to be inquisitive about strangers, but they do not seem to be. They just look with empty eyes and then turn back to whatever they may be doing. One or two booths are open in the bazaar – a narrow street that leads past the walls of the citadel – but the rest are shuttered and look abandoned. I have never been in a place so sighing with the sorrows of death.

I walked down the empty street to the gateway of the citadel, which has a big, square façade, sixty feet high or more. It has a good deal of debased sugar-cake-Moghul decoration, midget minarets and so on, and elements of other styles too, including English early nineteenth-century. The building is more or less intact, though it looks as if it could do with some maintenance work. The big, wooden gates, which have hinges and crossbars of heavy wrought-iron, are closed: but a postern was open. I glanced up and down the street in case there might be someone willing to show me round and answer my questions. But there was no one.

The walls of the citadel tower above the little bazaar. They are only slightly less high than the triumphal entrance building itself, and at intervals along their summit are pottery ornaments, like tall thin vases with pointed lids – all in the work called 'kashi' in Sind: a blue or a near-purple glaze, sometimes a turquoise almost green. I went in through the postern.

The court stretched huge and empty. It must have had a certain grandeur when it was filled with people. There is a grove of trees planted in a careful rectangle to the left as you come in and, straight in front, on the far side of the court (which means some fifty yards ahead), is an octagonal pavilion, open-sided and made of wood, with a small onion dome above it, also of wood. But the pavilion is so small that only one man could find a place in it. He only. He could enter it by way of a private door in the wall behind, and appear before the people – but the people would be insulated from the pavilion by outer and inner parapets about breast-high, forming a sort of protective basin. The basin looks as if it were intended to be filled with water, but actually, on special days, the richer people would throw their jewels and gold and treasure into it: and the very poor would throw in whatever miserable belongings they had. They could not draw nearer than the basin, even if they dared. His men would then collect all this treasure and take it away to be stored in the inner citadel. The big, decorated wooden doors with the guardroom alongside, to the right of the pavilion, led to the inner citadel. Very privileged people might sometimes be allowed to pass through them; or else little people summoned for other purposes.

But the mosque would be for everybody. It fills one side of the great court and has its own fine marble court in front of it. It must have seemed very impressive to those who came to pray there, even if students of Indian architecture might not be much impressed. It is too 'late' (it was only begun in 1855, I believe) and the decoration is too fussy: but no one can deny that it is impressive in its gaudy, overwhelming way. It is covered all over with mosaic panels, sometimes flower patterns but more often geometrical designs like prayer rugs. Over the side doors are verses in calligraphic Persian script. He himself had written them, so the people said. And above the whole edifice sails a big gilded dome on an octagonal base. If you look at all carefully you will see that the dome is not centred over the mosque, as you might expect, but has been placed well to one side of centre.

I was moved – not, I think, by its beauty (which is questionable) but by the atmosphere of sorrow and bereavement. The court and the mosque should be filled with people and colour and the feel of life.

Pagāro – 1

The side doors of the mosque were open so I slipped off my shoes and went in, wondering who had remained to tend the place and keep it swept. An old man with a younger man behind him came forward with blank eyes.

They were agreeable enough, though very silent. They showed me round, making me count the forty wooden pillars that support the high, flat ceiling. The pillars are octagons, all of them, and painted in various shades of red and green and a darkish tan. The ceiling is broken up into a series of wooden panels, painted in the same colours as the pillars. The walls have conventional Moghul-type flower panels on them, rather naïvely, yet primly, painted. Some mats lie in a dusty heap in one corner.

The old man beckoned me to the far wall where a door stood open. It had a heavy woollen fringe hanging over it, like the decorated fringes that hang from Sindi camel accoutrements. Someone had added cowrie shells.

'Wear this,' the old man said, handing me a large handkerchief. So I put it over my head, wondering why he allowed me to go bareheaded in one part of the mosque and not in another. I followed him through the door.

The shrine ... with the gilded dome above it. The air hung as still and heavy as a sadness. The Sixth is not there. Four of his five predecessors (and the father of the first of them) lie beneath a wood and metal canopy with open screens all round through which you can see the tombs. The Fifth lies outside the screen. He was the Sixth. Away in the corners are less important tombs, and it is only those of the saints that are draped and decorated and each surmounted by a prodigious turban. The old man said nothing at all. Perhaps he thought that I would not understand. After some time, when I left the shrine again, he stayed behind and I could see him kneeling in an empty space beside the tomb of the Fifth. His shoulders seemed to be shaking a little.

I left him there. There was a magic in the place, and a sort of interdiction. I felt almost as if I were trespassing: so I left the old man there and held out some money to the younger man, saying that he was to give it to the old man when he had finished with his prayers. The younger man looked at the money and shook his head. He refused to take it.

The doors leading to the inner citadel were barred: but the walls alongside them are not very high, as I discovered when I left the mosque: and by clambering up at a point near the wooden pavilion, I could get a glimpse over them. There was nothing to see. Nothing. The place had been razed to the ground – flat, empty and deserted. The gardens had gone back to jungle, with stone and rubble and masonry and the remains of majesty lying in the midst of it.

So I left. There was nothing to wait for in this desolate place. The Five were hidden in their tombs. The Sixth had 'gone' and no one knew where his body lay. The line, they said, had been destroyed and there could never be a Seventh.

* * *

That was in 1946, and I had never been to Pir-jo-Goth before.

In January, 1955, nine years later, when I came for the second time, the Seventh Pir Pagaro, King of Kings, Syed Shah-i-Mardān Shah the Second, had been out shooting crocodile for days on end: but he had returned now and I had been able to contact him by telephone from the railhead. He said he was sending me a jeep. The jeep would bring me to Pir-jo-Goth and he hoped I would stay with him for a while. He had the voice and speech of a cultivated Englishman. I had never met him, but he had heard from one of his uncles (who was a good friend of mine) that I much wanted to visit him, and he had at once issued an invitation. His *khalifa* would come in the jeep to fetch me.

The jeep was dusty. So was *Khalifa* Muhammad 'Alim, and so was the deaf mute he had with him in the back of the jeep. The *Khalifa* was probably fairly dark-skinned under the white dust: a round, lively face. He had brisk movements too – brisk for a Sindi, anyway. The deaf mute was called Gunga and as soon as he had

Pagaro – I

loaded my suitcase and bedroll into the back of the jeep and perched himself on top of it all, we set off.

It was easy to understand why my companions were so dusty, and in five minutes I was too. It is not very far to Pir-jo-Goth from the railhead – fourteen miles, possibly – but it is like ploughing through heavy seas of dust. The dust rises in your wake and is drawn forward into your slipstream and covers you with its white powder. The particles that miss their mark add themselves to the load of dust the cactus hedges bear. It might seem impossible to conduct a conversation with your windpipe so blocked with dust, but it is not. Even Gunga, who can't speak at all, joined in. The *Khalifa* talked and gesticulated incessantly as he drove, and Gunga accompanied him with his miming, leaning forward and begging me to include him in my laughter. Sometimes, if I laughed enough with him, he would take my hand and lay it against his cheek to show that he was pleased.

'I am the motor driver,' Gunga said with his hands and eyes, 'and this is the jeep that I drive – *whoosh!* Fast and far!'

Khalifa Muhammad 'Alim treated him with wonderful sweetness and egged him on to extravagances of mime that were even dangerous, perched there on a bedroll in the back of a bounding jeep. But nothing could daunt Gunga. He was about thirty, with a battered, unconquerable, smiling face. As we jolted and leapt and rolled ahead through the dust clouds, they told me in their different media all sorts of entertaining and mildly indecent things: and then, recognising that I was capable of absorbing more, and more gross, indecencies, their tales became more gross. I was sick with laughter and dust in the windpipe long before the walls of Pir-jo-Goth – the Citadel of the Pir – showed themselves in the distance.

'You said that Pir sain returned early this morning from his shooting?' I asked the *Khalifa*.

'Yes. Very early.'

The otaq at Pir-jo-Goth is more grandiose than the otaq at Sehwan-Sharif, but it is on the same general lines. A good deal larger, however, and more modern. Not that it is modern in any absolute sense; it looks, in effect, like an up-country schoolhouse, or a dak bungalow of fifty years ago. The grand part of it contains two large bedrooms, with a bow-fronted reception room between them. Each bedroom has what passes for a bathroom attached to it – and it is indeed a room with a tin tub, a slatted footboard and a commode in it. But there is no water, except what may be brought in from outside, in buckets. In front of the otaq is a garden with a big neem tree, and a tap that spurts its water into a low-bordered tank. I sat outside my room, waiting for I am not sure what, and watched the *Khalifa* take his bath.

He undressed down to his ballooning pantaloons. He proved to have a surprisingly good, muscled body, and looked much better stripped than dressed. Dressed, he is rather too short. Undressed, with no taller man nearby to give the scale, he is sturdy and well built. He wrapped his towel round his waist and discreetly wriggled out of his pantaloons. Then he stepped into the little tank and turned on the tap. The bathing went on for a very long time. He became rather darker as the colour of his skin emerged from its dust layers. The ears, the eyes, the nostrils: every detail was attended to, and finally he stretched up into the neem tree and picked himself a twig with which he began industriously rubbing at his teeth and gums. He wandered about the garden during this part of the performance, rubbing and spitting and hoicking, and talking about this and that with whoever might happen to be passing through, and with me as well.

A servant had put a tray of tea beside me. When I had finished it, they carried a couple of buckets of hot water into my bathroom and invited me to take a bath.

'Pir sain wishes you to be brought to him,' a servant said, as I came out again.

'Good. Then I will put on a suit.'

I felt that I should be correctly dressed for the first meeting. Pir Sain was, after all, the King of Kings. But having put on a suit and sat around for a while awaiting the summons, nothing happened. They brought me another tray of tea, probably to comfort me, and I asked when I was to see Pir sain.

Pagāro – I

'When he comes out of his *haveli bangla*,' they said. *Bangla* is, of course, for bungalow: and *haveli* – a flower – here evidently meant the purdah quarters, the harem, where Pir sain's wife would be living. But no one could reach him there in order to ask. It was soon clear, moreover, that no one could ask such a question in any case. It would not be for a man to ask the King of Kings when he would do this or that. God alone knew.

'He is tired from his shooting,' they said hopefully.

I sat about a bit longer: in fact I sat about for a couple of hours in my formal suit, and grew restive.

'Perhaps Pir sain does not know that his guest has arrived at all?' I suggested.

'No one can say anything, when Pir sain is in his *haveli bangla*.'

'Then, if no one can say anything, I think I will go for a walk and see the town,' I said.

'But what if Pir sain should awake and come out of *haveli bangla* and should ask if his guest has arrived and should say for his guest to be brought to him and be told that …'

'In that case,' I said firmly, having considered the problem while the man went burbling on in his anxiety, 'in that case, since the little town is not much bigger than a village and I cannot become lost in it, you should send scouts in all directions and one of them will instantly discover me (*Insha' Allah*) and bring me to Pir sain.'

So I went walking. The otaq stands within fifty yards of the citadel's triumphal gateway, but outside it. Since my last visit, everything had been tidied up. There was an air of movement and prosperity, and of happiness too, in the newly plastered façade and in the huge towering walls with their 'kashi' work ornament. The bazaar shops were open now and people wandered about, picking over the merchandise. A biggish group of ruffianly looking men sat in the dust outside the citadel, waiting, and almost as soon as I had passed on my way through the bazaar, a man with mad eyes rose and left them. He came up to me, making no salute, and spoke in Urdu so bad that I had difficulty in following him at first, though it was clear that he intended to accompany me. My 'bodyguard' (for

I was already accompanied by one of the several men who seemed to have been detailed to serve me) demurred, but the man insisted, and as I could see no harm in it I told him to come too. He spoke in a gabbling voice and frequently clutched at my arm, whereat my 'bodyguard' would try to disengage him.

'There is none, none, none that can stand beside him!' he exclaimed, and it was not difficult to guess that he was referring to Pir Pagaro, so I agreed.

'NONE!' His voice came out in a big shout.

'It is true, but *shush*,' said the 'bodyguard'.

'None,' he repeated, but more softly.

'What is your name?' I asked him.

'Majna.'

'I am agreeing with you too, Majna,' I said.

He was quieter again now. Probably he had doubted if I really believed.

We wandered through the bazaar, skirting the citadel walls and turning, where they turned, at right angles down a side street of the bazaar. About a hundred yards farther on there was a gap in the citadel walls. Part of the wall was being rebuilt from the foundations. A gang was working on it, carrying materials up a long diagonal ramp to the top. High on the battlements an ibex stood, majestically alone. I could see that it wore a collar. Perhaps it was just taking a substitute for the air of mountains. We passed through a breach in the walls and walked on, through gardens and orchards of fruit. Order had started to come back to the gardens of the inner citadel. A building like a little bullring stood shadowed by trees: a *shikar garh*, into which wild animals would be driven to be shot by Pir sain and his guests from a barricaded tower in the centre of the enclosure. The 'guns' would reach the central tower by way of a bridge built out from the surrounding wall. Wild boar would often be the target – creatures both dangerous and tabu.

Majna talked on, as if hysteria were fairly near the surface. I think my 'bodyguard' would have preferred him to remain quiet.

Pagāro – I

'There is no one to stand beside him, no one! He is alone, our King of Kings. If he tells us, his people, to kill, we will kill – even if we must die too – for what is death? We will die at his bidding. But who could give such an order? Who? Only our Pir sain, and he would not, for he is good and kind.' He paused and a little cloud seemed to pass across his face: 'But where is he who came before? Where?' He suddenly became wild and turned on me, not with menace but with a mad sorrow: 'YOU KILLED HIM!'

I think I must have remained silent for a moment. My 'bodyguard' was watching closely: Majna stood there with his eyes screwed up and his mouth twitching. Then I said: 'Good things and bad – they all come from God. And Pir Pagaro is with you once again.'

Majna was nodding in a strange mechanical way as we walked on.

He said: 'The wicked proclaimed that there was a boy in a box – but it is not true.'

* * *

Nevertheless it was true. It was also true that Pir Pagaro the Sixth had died on the gallows, convicted by the British of 'waging war against the King'. It was in 1943, the formal climax to something that had been building itself up in a strange manner for more than a hundred years.

The trial was by court martial, behind locked doors. Very little was ever made public. Pir Pagaro was sentenced and hanged, and his body was taken for burial to a secret place: and when the news of his execution was announced, thousands upon thousands of his followers refused to believe that he was dead – for how could it be possible to destroy the indestructible? 'He is not dead,' they repeated stubbornly: 'for if they had killed him, night everlasting would have fallen upon the world. The sun still rises – though in sadness now. He is only "gone" from us for a time ...' And this they believed with all their hearts – that he would come back to them one day.

Perhaps the phenomenon of Pir-jo-Goth is something that can only be intelligible to the eye and the ear of the heart – the heart of an initiate. The facts are there, for those who choose to puzzle their heads over them, but what can be made of them? A true saint, a Turban and a Flag: attempted murder, a successful murder: God and his holy people ...

The true saint was descended from a Lakiari Syed who generations before had left Sehwan-Sharif to 'secure a separate spiritual foothold in the hearts of the people, and earn a living', and by the time he died, which was in 1818, he had established a new pirship 'of the Turban and the Flag' with some nine hundred thousand adoring *murids*. It is uncertain whether he had nominated his successor to this new throne before he died, but clear that Sibghatullah, one of his thirteen sons, assumed the Turban of Pirship and that Yasin, another of the sons, coveted it so passionately that he tried to kill Sibghatullah in order to get it for himself. The attempt failed and Yasin was put to flight by Pir Sibghatullah's followers who thereupon made a solemn declaration. From that day onwards, they declared, they would honour only the wearer of the Turban himself: no part of their allegiance, nor even of their respect, would they accord to their Pir's relatives – whether brothers or sons, or cousins or uncles or no matter whom – because of what Yasin had tried to do.

Pir Sibghatullah was much touched by their loyal address and marked the occasion by granting them a special title of honour – 'Hur' – which is pronounced 'hoorr' with a very light vowel and a short, hard, rolling 'r'. Hur meant 'holy', and the recipients of the honour were very pleased with it. In fact everybody at Pir-jo-Goth seems to have been content now. It was true that Yasin, in escaping, had apparently made off with the second of the two emblems of pirship – the Flag: but it was the Turban that really mattered, and Sibghatullah had that firmly planted on his head, and his feet planted firmly in the hearts of his people: he had become, in fact, first Pir of the *Păg* – or Turban: Pir Pagaro. And at a place called Hala, a long way down the valley, Yasin had before very long established himself as Pir of the *Jhando* – or Flag: Pir Jhandewaro. The Turban and the Flag were from now on as separate as the two pirships they represented. Live and let live.

Pagāro – I

But a couple of generations later, in the eighteen-sixties, when the third Pir of the Turban was on the throne at Pir-jo-Goth, and the third Pir of the Flag on his at Hala, the principle of live-and-let-live had slipped a little. The third Flag Pir was proving to be a remarkable young man, saintly, ambitious, capable (they said) of working little miracles. The third Pir of the Turban, on the other hand, was not remarkable in the least, and he had absolutely nothing but his inherited nobility to rely upon, and it was not proving quite enough. Already a good many disciples had been weaned away from the Turban to the Flag – and in addition there was a beautiful young woman who had been weaned away by the Flag Pir too – though for less spiritual purposes – and this young woman happened to be betrothed already to one of Pagaro's Hurs. So when the news flashed over the grapevine that the Flag Pir had been ambushed and murdered while taking a bath on the river's brink, everybody knew perfectly well who had done it: and the British – who had annexed Sind in 1843 and were firmly in the saddle by now – knew too: they arrested both Pir Pagaro and the Hur in question and charged them with the murder of the Flag Pir. The outcome of the trial was that Pir Pagaro was acquitted for lack of evidence, and his Hur was hanged.

The point to be stressed is not at all Pir Pagaro's unproven guilt, but his reactions to the indignities of a trial. He was enraged, not only with the British, but with everyone in sight, including his Hurs: and the Hurs, far from being disheartened by his rage, were driven to new ecstasies of love for him. A great new wave of awe and emotion swept over them. It was difficult to explain it, perhaps, because to look at him you might suppose that Pir Pagaro the Third was the most ordinary and uninspiring of mortals – but nevertheless he was *theirs*, he belonged to his Hurs, and they to him, his humiliation had been their humiliation, and now that he had come through the ordeal miraculously unscathed (because everyone knew that he was guilty), and was seen to be in a state of world-shaking fury, it was almost like a triumph. His triumph was, in fact, his Hurs' triumph. And it was now that the Hurs began to perceive the truth, or part of it. Pir Pagaro was far more than a saint or a mystic or a worker of little miracles: Pagaro was far, far above such trifles, a being of an infinitely higher order. In fact it was evident that Pagaro must partake in some very intimate fashion of the Nature of God – oneness with the Divine Essence or something metaphysical of the sort: he was, so to say, on an equality with God. Was he, perhaps, even God Himself? And then they saw it: he *was* God Himself! Alone, Supreme! HE! And once this tremendous truth had been vouchsafed to the Hurs, everything else fitted neatly into perspective. The murder of the Flag Pir, for example: it was clear that Pir Pagaro had murdered his cousin as an act of divine retribution for aspiring to cousinship with God. And then the Hurs remembered how the first Flag Pir had tried to kill the first Pir Pagaro all those years before, and how from the very outset their Hur ancestors had foreseen everything and had denounced those who by the accident of birth should claim blood relationship with Pir Pagaro.

Pagaro was God. And his Hurs – or in any case the inner circle of his Hurs – were God's people, placed high above the common man. Pagaro's followers were divided into two distinct categories – the inner circle of initiates, and the rank and file. The rank and file would be called *Salimis*; they would respect their pir and contribute to his revenues in the ordinary way, but they were not initiates. The true, inner brotherhood would be the *Farqi* Hurs, the separate, holy people (for '*Farqi*' is derived from the Arabic root meaning 'separate') in service of the pir and pledged to absolute devotion to him of mind, body, soul and estate. They were his creatures, their women his women: they must obey his commands down to the very smallest detail and as often as they were permitted a glimpse of him they must cast all they possessed at his feet.

Pir Pagaro the Third, that very ordinary man, was certainly not proof against such extravagances. He probably liked it very much, this idea of a separate, holy brotherhood, dedicated to his person, and he must have watched with interest and pleasure as the *Farqi* Hur code became established and their rules of conduct were laid down – special green clothing and a special turban, oaths of allegiance involving death for the least infraction: they would take food only with brother *Farqis*, they would salute no one but their pir, each other they would greet by folding their arms across the breast. But there were to be no rules about sex: any *Farqi* might sleep with the wife or daughter or sister of any brother *Farqi* and this would be a matter for congratulation. They were poor people for the most part, these *Farqis*, but what they lacked in treasure for Pagaro, they certainly made up in devoted service – and there were plenty of well-to-do *Salimi* followers who could be counted upon to fill the Pir's coffers. Even so, it was remarkable how much the poverty-stricken *Farqis* were managing to give their pir ...

It was indeed remarkable how much the *Farqi* Hurs could give, now that the brotherhood was established and was spreading across Sind. They were not a tribe, or a class: they were a brotherhood, and soon few villages in Sind were without a cell of *Farqis* in their midst. Anyone who seemed suitable could gain admittance, provided he swore the terrible oaths of allegiance. Non-Muslims were admitted too – Hindus and Sikhs. The Hurs did not even insist upon circumcision: all they demanded was absolute obedience to the Hur code, absolute loyalty as between each Hur and his fellows. And in return ... well, the world was theirs! They might rob and rape and loot, and pillage and burn: they might indulge their appetites exactly as they pleased, they might murder and mutilate, anything was permissible that was done to the glory of their pir or to bring gold to his coffers. The criminal elements in the countryside flocked to the *Farqis* knowing that with them they would find protection against their enemies, the police.

Pagaro may have become God, but he had certainly lost control. God's holy and separate people were ranging the countryside, pillaging and killing. The authorities would manage to break up one gang of bandits only for another to appear somewhere else, and no one ever dared give evidence against a Hur because of the certainty of vengeance. The British demanded that Pir Pagaro use what influence he had to control his people – but he was helpless, and when he ordered them to desist, they respectfully took no notice of his orders because they could see at once that 'the Pir's wish in this matter was not the unaffected and pure wish of the Pir's own soul'. The Hurs had created a god in their own image and did as they pleased in his name – and indeed the Pir's small son only narrowly escaped murder at their hands for presuming to enter the Presence with his shoes on.

It is no part of my purpose to detail the various Hur uprisings nor the measures that Government took to subdue them, except to record that it was a menace on a scale so alarming that by the turn of the century it had become necessary to declare the Hurs a criminal tribe within the meaning of the Act designed to deal with such problems. Corrective Settlements were established in which offenders might be held indefinitely, and schools were opened within the settlements in the hope that the children, at least, might be weaned from the appalling doctrines of their fathers. And there was no doubt that these measures produced results. The countryside grew calmer.

But meanwhile Pir Pagaro the Third was dead, and the Fourth had died too. The Fifth was on the throne at Pir-jo-Goth as Syed Shah-i-Mardan Shah – as helpless as his predecessors had been in the face of the Hurs who upheld his godhead and filled the vaults of his treasury. Yet he must carry on somehow. He had his duties to perform. One of his duties was to go on progresses amongst his peoples, and the progress he undertook at the end of 1912 was particularly successful, it seems. The Hurs had literally tumbled over each other to do him honour and shower at his feet all they possessed in the world (or in any case a good deal of it): but when it was all over, these same loyal Hurs were obliged to embark upon a campaign of pillage and the murder that so often went with it, at least equivalent in enthusiasm to their recent outpourings of treasure at the divine feet – for their pockets had been emptied. The countryside was in a state of panic once again.

Pir Pagaro the Fifth wrung his hands in his distress: he was afraid of his Hurs and afraid of the British, and it was indeed difficult to know what he could do. He wrote to the Commissioner-in-Sind begging him to arrange for the 'wholesale removal of this vicious tribe from even the confines of Sind, and that not a child, even, of theirs be allowed to stay'. There is no doubt that in a way he meant

Pagāro – I

it: no doubt, either, that he knew as well as the Commissioner-in-Sind that deportation on such a scale was out of the question. Where could they be sent, these thousands upon thousands of mad, violent, fanatic criminals?

Syed Shah-i-Mardan Shah, Fifth Pir Pagaro, died in 1922, and his fourteen-year-old son succeeded to the throne as Syed Sibghatullah Shah the Second, Sixth Pir Pagaro. And now, for the first time since the Hur brotherhood had come to flower, they were to be blessed with a god who would prove worthy of them.

* * *

Over in the little District Headquarters town of Sukkur, with its suspension bridge and the Indus flowing by, with its biscuit factory, its clocktowers, its dusty trees, the Collector of the District must have watched uneasily as the reports came in and were added to the file marked Pir Pagaro.

Hur outrages were commonplace enough. There were established formulae for dealing with them: you must be ready for them and act ruthlessly: but this was something of a different sort. Pir-jo-Goth was perhaps fifteen miles from Sukkur as the crow flies; not very far off; but the walls of its citadel were high and the Hurs guarded their secrets jealously. Yet little rumours would leak out, to be picked up in the bazaars and teashops and whorehouses by the sort of men who live by the selling of information. The stories these men carried were disturbing in a new way. Hitherto the successive Pirs of Pagaro might have been stupid or weak, venal of course, and often avaricious, but they had been the victims rather than the masters of their strange inheritance. It could not be said of them that they had been evil men in the context of contemporary Sind, only that they had been too weak to prevent the horrible crimes that were committed in their names. But Sibghatullah, Sixth Pir Pagaro, this boy ... He was still only a youth yet if reports were true he was already showing his Hurs that he was their master and the indications were very disquieting.

The Hurs were watching the boy grow too – with a passionate, greedy devotion: for here, surely, at last, was the true God! – young as yet, but filled with the most resplendent promise! They brought him their women, their sisters and wives and daughters, they nourished him upon debauchery, they must have stood back to marvel at his appetites and at his stamina, and marvelled again at the fits of brutal, bludgeoning violence that would come down upon him sometimes like an ecstasy. It seemed as if he had been born with the dark knowledge of the universe already within him, and they worshipped him – worshipped him when he loved them or when he dishonoured them, when he killed them or commanded them to kill others, for this was the golden age and this the true God!

* * *

Sibghatullah was growing into a large man, black-bearded, handsome, with eyes as calm as planets. He had suffered from smallpox in his childhood and the disease had left his skin pitted with the scars of it. But already he had a majesty of presence that was commented upon even by those who claimed to be unafraid. He had an agile mind and, unlike his forebears, he gloried in his godhead. He was God! Let those ridiculous little Englishmen over in Sukkur, those Collectors and District Magistrates and Superintendents of Police, pore over their files and shake their heads! His world was his own to do with as he pleased.

Men disappeared from Pir-jo-Goth and were not seen again. Strange things happened and the people went about their affairs with closed faces, and when the authorities inquired into the whereabouts of X or Y, or into the identity of a body that someone had found, no one seemed to know anything – yet everybody knew. It had always been like this in dealing with the Hurs: no one dared to speak. Government could do nothing if the public were not prepared to help: their hands were tied, they could do nothing. But one day a Sindi woman called Mariam managed to slip away from Pir-jo-Goth to Sukkur to lodge a complaint with the authorities.

Pagāro – I

She was in terrible distress. Indeed her distress must have been overwhelming for otherwise her fear of retribution would have smothered it. She said that her son Ibrahim had been taken by Pir Pagaro and was being held in his inner citadel – his 'Kot', as it was called. The authorities must have tried to calm the woman, and certainly they questioned her and promised to do what they could to secure her son's release: yet to them it cannot have seemed an affair of very great moment. There were other matters much more serious on the files. It was even doubtful if they could do anything for the woman, but they would try, and meanwhile her deposition would go on record, along with all the rumours and whispers.

Very shortly after, the woman Mariam was found murdered – and no one could doubt that Pagaro had had her killed for daring to speak.

Government took action. An inquiry was instigated and on the strength of its finding a charge of abetment to murder was laid against Pir Pagaro. The case was tried in Sukkur but the charge could not be proved and the Court discharged the Pir – yet everybody knew that he was guilty. In due course, several years later, sufficient evidence had accumulated to make action possible again – the police raided the citadel at Pir-jo-Goth, armed with search warrants, and there found the murdered woman's son, Ibrahim – the Boy in the Box. Pir Pagaro and four accomplices were charged with 'the wrongful confinement of the boy Ibrahim'. This was in 1930. The Pir was twenty-two years old.[1]

The charge was trifling – or so the Pir must have thought: but he could not have failed to see that his liberty was at stake. He engaged counsel to defend him: the best counsel in the land – Mr Mohamed Ali Jinnah, who twenty-seven years later was to bring into being the new sovereign state of Pakistan. No sooner had Mr Jinnah arrived in Sind and been shown into his young client's presence than he protested with formal vehemence against the manner of his reception. Mr Jinnah was not prepared to be met at the station by a

---

1. The police also discovered a quantity of unlicensed arms and ammunition which were the subject of a charge against him that was tried separately.

dilapidated old motorcar when the Pir's garages were filled with fine cars. The Pir explained: of course, he had fine cars in his garages: but did not Mr Jinnah realise that the Hurs would have killed him instantly, had they seen him in a car that their Pir was accustomed to ride in? One must imagine that the two men watched each other in a wary silence: the one lean, pale, ascetic-looking, already conscious of his great destiny: the other a young man filled with unnatural powers that he was only now beginning to comprehend. But for the moment there were different problems to be considered, notably this matter of the 'boy in the box'.

For all his great brilliance there was nothing that Mr Jinnah could do to secure his client's acquittal. Pir Sibghatullah, 'the first accused', and four of his men were convicted and sentenced. The little Sukkur courtroom was hushed as Mr Udharam, the City Magistrate, read out his judgement.

'This Ibrahim …' read Mr Udharam, smoothing his papers on the desk before him …

'This Ibrahim is the elder son of that unfortunate Mariam for causing whose murder the first accused was tried in this court and discharged. At the time the story opens he was a comely lad of 14 or 15 years of age and an inhabitant of Pir-jo-Goth, the village in which the first accused resided behind the wide walls of prodigious height of his "kot". One day, about four years ago, Ibrahim was taken into this 'kot' in the company of some other men, young and old, to plaster the roofs of the buildings that rose within it. When the day was drawing to a close, the first accused's eye fell on him as he stood on one of the roofs and he took such a powerful fancy to him that he had hardly passed by when he sent one of his servants, Allahdino by name, with an offer of service under him. Hardly daring to refuse, Ibrahim nevertheless begged for time to consult his relations and requested Allahdino to come back for his answer on the third day.'

Could it be already four years ago? Pir Sibghatullah, 'first accused', must have sat there, half-listening, half-remembering, as the voice droned on about 'this Ibrahim'. What business was it of these presumptuous fools? He must surely have longed to

Pagāro – I

rise up, throw his arms wide and bring down the wrath and the thunder upon them all – but he sat there, half-listening, perhaps, half-remembering, he, Pir Pagaro, Fountain of Benevolence, King of Kings, God: HE must sit there as the City Magistrate's voice went droning on ... Ibrahim and his family ... so poor ... tempted by money ... the offer was accepted, and in due course Ibrahim presented himself at the 'kot' and duties were assigned to him: personal attendance upon the Pir and the cleaning of the donkey engine that worked the lighting plant in the citadel. The judgement droned on and on with lilt of a bad-fairy story ...

'Twenty or twenty-five days passed without anything happening to mar their peace. On the twenty-sixth day, while working in the engine room, Ibrahim upset a glass oiling-cup and broke it. Its loss, trifling though it was, put out the first accused to such an extent that he tied Ibrahim's arms behind his back and flogged him, and when this did not suffice to abate the violence of his passions, he shaved the boy's eyebrows, plucked hair from his eyelashes, blackened his face with oil and soot, and commanded his servants to void urine over him. When Ibrahim had stood on his legs in this state for about an hour, his arms were untied and he was given a bath. He was not, however, allowed to leave the "kot", for fear that his shaved eyebrows would proclaim to the people at large the way the first accused treated his servants. Two or three days passed in this manner but there was no rest for Ibrahim. Although his eyebrows were painted in with lamp-black, yet he could not look in the faces of his fellow-servants without a feeling of humiliation which was probably the more acute as the shaved eyebrows had spoiled the prettiness of his face.'

He had lied to his master, the little swine! He had begged leave to visit his wife, claiming that she had just been delivered of a son, and when permission was granted had run out of the citadel, borrowed thirty rupees from his uncle on some pretext or another and had made for the nearest railway station. But he hadn't got away with it: the Hurs knew, and the Hurs went after him to the distant place where he had hoped to hide himself. They had caught him and dragged him back to Pir-jo-Goth – and from then onwards a guard had been set to watch the boy, three men in turn. The Collector of Sukkur heard rumours, of course, and some time later wrote demanding that the Pir dismiss 'three of his servants'. Well, what did it matter which 'three men' kept guard over the boy? Three men were dismissed and three more appointed: and the boy was told that the Collector was very angry, and that it was therefore better for him to remain in concealment.

The voice went droning on ...

'This short period over, their old life resumed its sway until nearly twelve months passed away, and preparations for the first accused's tour amongst his *murids* began ... He proceeded on his tour, taking with him Ibrahim, who did not, however, join his cortège, but travelled like his women in a closed litter on the back of a camel. After seven months of touring in this manner, they returned to Pir-jo-Goth.'

It was now 1928. Almost at once they had started out again on what was to be the Pir's great Hindustan tour, to places farther afield than those he had visited in the tour just ended. He had his *murids* well beyond the confines of Sind – in the Punjab and Baluchistan and Delhi and Simla, in Bombay, Karachi of course: all these places. And Ibrahim came too. But within three short weeks they had returned to Pir-jo-Goth. There had been difficulties and irritations. Interfering officials in Sukkur, and again in Quetta and again in Karachi, had all demanded that he release the boy Ibrahim. What had it got to do with them? Was he not Pir Pigaro? Could he not keep a boy if he chose to, as he kept women and they kept dogs? Could he not chain his boy to one of his men if he wished to? Perhaps the Pir even sat back to wonder how it could be that this boy had become so necessary to his life, this loved and hated creature, despised, humiliated, dishonoured, beaten, chained to his captors, spat upon yet needed.

It had been beneath the Pir's dignity to admit discussion of his personal affairs: he had simply denied that Ibrahim was his prisoner – and he had told Ibrahim this: it explained in part why it was impossible to release him now, for you can't release what you do not hold within your power. Perhaps it was at this stage that he

Pagāro – I

told the boy how he had ordered the murder of the woman Mariam, his mother.

Another year passed. It must have been some time in 1929 that the Collector of Sukkur again demanded Ibrahim's release – and he would have done better not to interfere, because it only meant that Ibrahim must henceforth be confined not merely to the inner citadel but to one room in the Pir's own house. Ibrahim had cried and gone on his knees and begged at least to be permitted to see his wife and baby son. And when permission was refused he had threatened to run away. Run away from Pir-jo-Goth? Was he mad?

From that time onwards Ibrahim was kept permanently in chains. He had been prisoner in the 'kot' for more than three years by now.

And still the voice went droning on in the stifling heat of the courtroom. It was late August. Sind is an inferno in August. Windows must be shuttered close in an attempt to keep the heat at bay, but it comes in and the flies come in with it, somnolent heavy heat, and flies as somnolent and heavy, and dust – nothing can keep them back. Mr Udharam read on. He had reached a new element in his recitation: the flight from Pir-jo-Goth of the Pir's mother, his sister, his younger brother and an aunt. It was not only the miserable Ibrahim who must suffer. Anyone, at any time, might be the victim of the Pir's ungovernable, unpredictable violence: and certainly all those who presumed to be related by blood to him, to the Fountain of Benevolence, to God, must live in special terror of their lives, for the Hurs had a black hatred of them. Not that anybody spoke of these people as the Pir's relatives: it was sufficient for the Hurs that they should exist, and remarkable only that they were still alive. For months now they had been planning their escape, it seems, and the plan succeeded. They reached Sukkur in safety and were taken under the protection of Government. They had a good deal to tell the Collector.

And so it went on. The more peremptory the demands of the officials in Sukkur, the more strict became Ibrahim's confinement. A senior police officer arrived at Pir-jo-Goth 'on tour' and encamped there. The Pir knew what he was after: the police had been far too active and inquisitive of late, one way and another. Additional precautions were necessary. Ibrahim was now required to pass his nights in a box. It had a small circular hole in the bottom through which it was presumed that he would get sufficient air to breathe. He was given a quilt and a drinking cup, and an earthenware pot in which to answer the calls of nature. The Pir had thought of everything. But the police officer left Pir-jo-Goth and nothing had actually happened. Even so it was best to keep Ibrahim in the box. The police might reappear suddenly.

And so it went on. Soon a fresh batch of terrified refugees managed to escape from the Pir's citadel. This time it was not relatives but three of his maidservants. How they got away was a mystery, but they did, and they too claimed sanctuary in Sukkur. They had even more than the Pir's mother and sister to tell the authorities.

It was the Pir himself who went after the absconding maidservants, and before leaving Pir-jo-Goth he left instructions that in no circumstances was Ibrahim to be allowed out of the box in his absence. And for the seven or eight days of the Pir's fruitless visit to Sukkur, Ibrahim left his box only for one, or possibly two short airings. The hole in the bottom of the box was, after all, not quite sufficient for ventilation and the Pir's men must have felt that the boy ought at least to be still alive when his master returned. So they took him in chains for a walk in the gardens this once, or maybe twice, and then put him back in his box. Nor, when the Pir returned, was he let out of the box except for short spells of work in the engine room.

Then suddenly the police reappeared at Pir-jo-Goth. Ibrahim's prison had to be changed. He was now locked in another box in a corner of the gardens: but on thinking it over the Pir must have seen that this was a bad place; the boy would be safer inside: so he was transferred to another box, a much smaller one this time: one that could be accommodated in a little passage that ran at the back of the Pir's house. And it was there that two days later the police found the box, after an elaborate search in the presence of the Pir himself.

'*Don't touch it!*' shouted the Pir, his face contorted with rage. It

Pagāro – I

was past all bearing that these dogs of infidels, these swine, should yet have power to disturb the tranquillity of the King of Kings. 'Don't touch it!' – and he shouted to them that the box contained a mad Hur who had begged to be locked up in this manner so that he might be prevented from biting people.

The police opened the box.

When Ibrahim was taken out he was 'so pale and emaciated that Mr England (the policeman) was led to describe him as a ghost and pale as death'. Not much was left now of the prettiness of his face.

The Pir laid a finger to his lips, enjoining him to silence – and then explained how Ibrahim had been enclosed in the box at his own desire, for fear that the police would find him and take him away. Mr Udharam, the City Magistrate, had a comment to make on this in his judgement:

'It does not commend itself to reason ... Ibrahim had nothing to fear from the police: if he did not want to leave the first accused and the pleasures he enjoyed in his company, he had simply to say so to the police, to be left; severely alone.'

Mr. Udharam passed his judgement:

'In these circumstances I convict all five accused for offences punishable under Sections 344 and 346 of the Indian Penal Code ...'

– a total sentence of five years' rigorous imprisonment, plus a fine, in the case of the Pir: and six months' rigorous imprisonment in the case of each of the four other accused, 'for they had been no more than the first accused's tools'. The fine – if recovered – was to be given in compensation to Ibrahim. He signed: Udharam, C. M. Sukkur. 28-8-1930 – and he added his orders regarding disposal of the property concerned in the case:

'The box and the drinking-cup and quilt-cover to be sold and the proceeds credited to Government. The earthenware pot to be destroyed. The coats to be returned to Ibrahim.'

During the years that Pir Pagaro the Sixth was to spend in jail he had plenty of time to consider the future and to dream dreams about it.

* * *

When was it that Pir Sibghatullah first saw in himself the fulfilment of an old prophecy? Was it during those years of imprisonment? Was it in fact an old prophecy? No one seemed to have spoken of it before, yet towards the close of the nineteen-thirties it was cropping up all over the place, in casual teashop conversation, in the bazaars and villages of Sind, as if it were an established piece of folklore that everyone had always known. People ascribed it to one 'Abdul Rahim Gharori – but I do not know who this man was, nor even when he lived. There were several versions.... 'A pir who has suffered oppression shall achieve the Throne of Sind.' Or possibly: 'A pir who is pock-marked shall achieve the Throne of Sind', or else it was that: 'The Throne of Sind shall fall to a pir who has made the pilgrimage to Mecca' – the *Hajj* of the Muslims. And some people were now saying that a great king was destined to arise when the Indus should be stemmed near Sukkur – and everyone could see the enormous barrage that had been thrown across the Indus at Sukkur in the early thirties, while Pir Sibghatullah was in jail.

Pir Sibghatullah was released from jail in November 1936, having served six years of the combined sentences he had received in the case for 'wrongful confinement' and in the case tried separately under the Arms Act. He was carried home in triumph in a train specially chartered by his Hurs, and within a short time he went on the *Hajj* to Mecca. He was the first of his line to have made the pilgrimage, he claimed to be first to have suffered oppression, and he was certainly the first to carry the scars of the smallpox. Was it he, then, who was destined to become King of Sind? He was twenty-eight now, and possessed of a terrible power. He was much courted by politicians who knew that by a nod or a gesture he could direct the votes of thousands upon thousands. His arrogance – and

Pagāro – I

his envy – were boundless. He seems to have been particularly envious of His Highness the Aga Khan, for the Aga Khan too derived his powers through a mystic chain of authority back into the dawn of Islam: but the Aga Khan occupied a position of high honour and respect throughout the world and was weighed against gold, whereas Pagaro ... He thumped his chest and trumpeted his ridiculous challenge, a muscle-man at a country fairground: 'I will produce for you ten Hurs who for my sake will confess to a murder they have not done and will gladly hang for it! Can the Aga Khan produce one such, even?' Yet it was true: the Aga Khan could not, and Pagaro manifestly could.

You would probably have to go back to the eleventh century to find a parallel to Pagaro's dominion over his people – back to the Old Man of the Mountains and his Assassins and the fortress of Alamout, high in the mountains south of the Caspian sea. It is said that the Old Man of the Mountains, whose name was Hassan ben Sabbah, had such power over his followers that at a nod from him any one of them would readily throw himself from the ramparts of Alamout into the abyss below; and it is believed that the mainspring of this power lay in the ritual of the initiation ceremony through which each novice had to pass before being accepted into the body of 'those who sacrifice themselves' – as ben Sabbah called his men. He would cause each novice to be drugged and brought to a garden where the loveliest of girls awakened him; and for two days or three he would remain there, taking his pleasure of the girls and of wine and sherbets and fruits, and tasting the joys of paradise. Then he would be drugged once more and carried back to the harsh realities of Alamout: but he would have learnt that provided he gave his life to his master to do with as he wished, this paradise of which he had been given a foretaste by his master's grace, would be his for eternity. The drug that Hassan ben Sabbah administered to his novices was hashish, and to the outside world these murderous dedicated men who did ben Sabbah's bidding became the Assassins. Hashish to this day is capable of opening the gates of artificial heavens and hells to those who take it. But Pir Pagaro could exact obedience from his Hurs to the point of self-immolation even without the use of drugs.

Pir Pagaro's ambition drove him on. Soon after the declaration of World War II, rumours of a private army were current: the Pir was believed to be recruiting, training and arming a large body of his Hurs and organising them on military lines. He was stocking an immense armoury. Such an undertaking could scarcely remain secret, so he caused it to be said that he was preparing to help the war effort. His personal contribution to the noble cause would be a body of Civic Guards: and in case the idea of Hurs as Civic Guards might in itself seem insufficiently reassuring to Government and to a public with a vivid memory, he made a donation of ten thousand rupees of his *murids'* money to the Sind War-Planes Fund.

But side by side with naïve public gestures of this sort came whispers of things a great deal stranger. Pir Sibghatullah was granting his Civic Guards the title of *Ghazi* – fighter in the cause of Allah and Islam. People who claimed to have witnessed the enrolment ceremony said that Sibghatullah was causing his recruits to be laid out before him on the ground, wrapped in shrouds: they were as dead men over whom he would go through the forms of a burial service. This done, he would address them as they lay in the silence of their shrouds …

'You have offered me your heads! Soon I shall have need of them. The British Government is engaged in war. My moment is coming. You have heard how the peoples rose at news of Mahatma Gandhi's arrest and imprisonment by the British? You have heard how splendidly they rose and fought for Gandhi's freedom? I too have suffered oppression at the hands of the British – and what did the Hurs do for their Pir? Nothing! You have miserably failed me. If it should happen that I call you, or that the British take me once again … Derail trains, cut communications, breach canals! Burn, pillage! Shed blood! KILL! FOR I AM TO BE KING OF SIND!'

He was obsessed with the dream of his destiny. He walked in clouds of hate and of the most glittering ambition.

Pagāro – I

He could not be left at large. Late in 1941 he was summoned to Karachi and required to live there – but he slipped away and returned to Pir-jo-Goth. He was brought back again and served with a notice under the Defence of India Rules compelling him to remain in Karachi, under surveillance. The moment had come. The Hurs knew their duty and set about doing it – sabotage, arson, murder. The Pir was arrested and removed to a place 'outside Sind', and by the end of the year a wave of Hur crime and terrorism had swept over Sind that had had no parallel even in the blackest days of the Hur brotherhood. Vast tracts of country were in a state of panic, cowed to the point of abject submission to the Hurs. Government did what they could with the forces at their disposal but the menace increased. In May 1942, the Hurs derailed the Lahore Mail train, butchering sixty-three passengers in circumstances of inspired brutality. On 1st June 1942, Martial Law was declared in the affected areas.

Gradually the situation was brought under control again, and in January 1943, Pir Sibghatullah was taken back to Sind to undergo trial by Court Martial. He was found guilty of 'waging war against the King', was sentenced to death and hanged. His 'kot' – the inner citadel at Pir-jo-Goth – was razed to the ground, his library was dispersed (the finest collection of Sindi manuscripts extant, or so it was said), the hoarded treasures of his home put up to auction. His two sons were taken to England, there to be brought up like the sons of English gentlemen.

* * *

It was in the summer of 1947 that the British finally relinquished their Indian Empire and partitioned the sub-continent between India and the newly created independent Muslim State of Pakistan. Sind fell to Pakistan. Policies that had seemed fit to the alien British Raj would not necessarily seem so to the Pakistanis, and amongst the policies that came into question was that in regard to the throne of the Pagaros, and the Hurs. Opinions were divided and indeed discussion dragged on for a long time, for it was a very vexed problem, but in 1952 a final decision was taken: the throne of the Pagaros was formally revived and the turn-of-the-century notification of the Hurs as a Criminal Tribe was abrogated.

A young man – until lately a student in England – was brought back to Sind and presented before the council of the Hurs, was accepted, and ascended the throne of his father and his father's fathers, as Pir Syed Shah-i-Mardan Shah the Second, Seventh Pir Pagaro.

5
Pagāro – II

WANDERING THROUGH THE ORCHARDS of Pir Pagaro's 'kot' that day of my return had taken longer than I realised at the time. It was already dusk when I freed myself of Majna – the wild, fanatical Majna – and came back to the otaq. There had still been no summons from the Pir. So I sat myself outside my room in the gloomy gloaming, a little irritated by so long a wait. It was getting colder as daylight died. The otaq seemed chilly and inhospitable. Men stood around and watched me, bored. I was bored too.

It was strange soon after to see the dark garden, and the still darker otaq, pricked suddenly here and there with points of orange light – all at once, as if someone had been waiting for the signal at each of these points, finger on the switch. Or else the explanation was that the engine and the dynamo it drove over there in the citadel – the donkey engine it had been the wretched Ibrahim's task to clean so long before – were only put to work when night fell, and then all the electric bulbs in all Pir-jo-Goth would spring simultaneously to life. The lights would come on, as they went off, at the bidding of a central control switch, perhaps: and Pir sain's programme of sleeping and waking would determine this, as everything else here. So when the otaq and the garden began to wink with little low-power oranges, I guessed that Pir sain was awake at last, and I was right. A servant came running to me: 'Please get ready – for Pir sain is arising now.'

I washed hurriedly and tidied myself up. For some reason the light in my bedroom was hooked low down in one of the corners. So I had to kneel in front of it to brush my hair, while a man held a shaving-mirror for me. Then they escorted me into the citadel.

The gates were open. The big, open piazza with its trees and mosque and miniature pavilion against the far wall was lit, but only very dimly. It was beautiful, seen thus. A group of men sat about outside the mosque. As I came nearer, one of them got up and detached himself from his fellows. It was Majna again, with a curious look in his eyes.

'You are going in now,' he said breathlessly. 'You are to wear this for your head.' He thrust a big, grubby handkerchief into my hands. 'Remember to take off your shoes and not to turn your back. You should stand thus, at the doors of our Lord's palace, your head lowered and your feet bare. You should await his order to come in. You should speak only if he requires you to speak. You have understood me?'

'Yes, yes,' I said – not irritably I think, but perhaps without much show of humility.

'Remember what I have told you,' Majna repeated, very clearly and in a louder voice. 'And put the handkerchief on now. Here! I will put it for you.'

He caught my arm and brusquely turned me so that I faced him. My 'bodyguard' made a little nervous protest and Majna shouted something in Sindi at him and some of the other people joined in too, taking sides, I suppose. Majna swung back towards me again, his voice louder than ever.

'I am telling you the proper way. Look! Put the handkerchief like *that* ...' – and he placed it squarely on my head. His companions mumbled in support of him. They had formed a half-circle round me by now. My 'bodyguard' looked anxious and confused. I felt sheepish: like a sheep that waits below the altar. Was there a sacrificial knife? Who held it? Majna? A postern in the big decorated doors leading to the 'kot' swung open and a man with a link-boy came out, followed by a small retinue. He found me in the shadows of the mosque wearing my grubby handkerchief-hat. Majna let go of me. The man looked at him but said nothing.

'Go!' Majna ordered. 'And do not forget what I have told you.'

'*Shush*,' said the 'bodyguard' – a token remonstrance so softly given that I doubt if Majna even heard it.

I walked at the head of a cavalcade into the 'kot'.

'Are those *Farqi* Hurs?' I whispered to the man beside me when we had passed through the gateway: and though he glanced sideways at me he made no reply. I tried again: 'I suppose that Majna and all those men outside the mosque are *Farqis*.'

'This way, kindly,' he said.

Our aura of yellow lantern light revealed nothing but flowerbeds newly planted: rose-bushes, a pomegranate here and there, a pathway with a chevron-edge of upturned bricks. Beyond was darkness. As we walked on, the whiteness of a tent gleamed milkily in the shadows to our left. A little farther still, to the right, was a small building with light streaming out sideways in a band across our pathway. It was as if a settler had staked a claim to a jungle site, cleared some part of it and established his camp there. I rearranged the handkerchief on my head, feeling rather embarrassed.

Pir Pagaro was sitting immediately opposite the entrance with a radio before him so big that I could only see part of him at first: his head, with thick black hair, a moustache, a white open-necked shirt and a pullover of fluffy lambswool. The pullover was baby-blue. He looked about twenty-six or twenty-seven, rather large and heavy – a languorous heaviness – and very similar in physical type to Pir Gul Muhammad Shah of Sehwan. The Lakiari strain was evident enough.

Did Pir sain get up to greet me? I am not sure now, but I imagine he did not. I am sure that the King of Kings ought not to have done so, anyhow. But he smiled and called out to me in his remarkably English voice:

'Don't take your shoes off, for heaven's sake! And whatever is that handkerchief doing on your head?'

I went in.

He sat me down on the sofa beside him. It was a very modernistic sofa, with streamlined wooden arms and a jazzy artificial-silk upholstery brocade. Pir Pagaro had kicked off his own Sindi slippers and looked very comfortable. His pantaloons were gleaming white and very full where they emerged from under an overcoat he had thrown across his knees. The room had no heating. There was a tin of '555' cigarettes perched on the radio. He offered me one.

We were in a small single-storeyed building, quite clearly of temporary construction: just the one room with whitewashed walls, open roof members and a long neon striplight sizzling away at white-heat on the ceiling. There were two or three fat armchairs, a couple of Persian rugs and an Afghan carpet. Several other men were with us in the room, but none of them was sitting on a chair, let alone on the sofa with Pir sain – and me. I was honoured, evidently. The others were crosslegged on the floor, heads bare, the unwound length of their turbans hanging round their necks like a priest's stole and falling down over their knees to the floor. They had overcoats wrapped round their legs too. One of them was smoking, I noticed. The conventions of respect towards the Pir Pagaro were different, it seemed, from those I had been accustomed to elsewhere.

Pir sain asked after my health, and while I was asking after his in my turn someone came in with a telephone on a mile of electric cable. For several minutes the room was filled with Pir sain's monologue – the lion's share of a conversation shouted in Sindi across canals and rivers, fields, jungle land. No doubt some courtier's ear was cocked attentively at the other end to receive the message. It took time, but when at last he had finished Pir sain turned back to me and said: 'I am well, thank you – but tired.'

I had been looking round the room and now he caught my eye. I think we both half smiled – as in connivance or church – and then he reorganised his features again. I did the same with mine.

He asked me what brought me to Pir-jo-Goth and I said 'You, Pir sain,' and he smiled again. Then he asked me if I cared about shooting and I saw that I must say no, both firmly and at once, because otherwise I would be trapped. So I said: 'No. Not at all.'

'I was thinking you might like to come out after crocodile with me. I've just been fixing up a shoot – that's what the telephone call was about.'

I *hm-m-m*'d a little.

'We'll have to start at three in the morning ...'

'Three!'
'Yes, three.'
What a terrible idea, three in the morning ...
'Yes,' he continued, 'you see, the place is a long way off.'
I took refuge in a diversion: 'They say crocodiles never eat men in the winter.'
He laughed at this and said: 'You know about crocodiles, then?'
I had to admit that I didn't, and decided not to tell him about Mister Peacock for fear that the Pirs of Pagaro possessed some totem creature still more remarkable and sacred than Mangho Pir's. I said: 'I have observed that crocodiles can move extremely fast on dry land – over a short distance.'

He was laughing at me quite openly now, at and with me. I didn't mind in the least if he supposed that I was frightened of crocodiles: but I was much concerned not to get up at three a.m. to do something hundreds of miles distant that I would not even do if it were in my back garden. I had not come all this way to Pir-jo-Goth for crocodiles.

'Yes, they can,' Pir sain admitted. 'Very fast. Over a short distance. But that's in flight, as a rule: not in attack. Incidentally they very seldom attack a man on dry land at all – even in summer.' He turned the knobs on the radio and changed the station: I don't know why he did this, because none of us listened to the new station any more attentively than to the first – except of course that there was no shutting one's ears to the sound of it. 'Still,' resumed Pir sain, raising his voice above the beautiful, shrill singing, 'you should be careful, even in winter. And if ever you want to cross a river and can see crocodile in it, remember to cross downstream of them.'

I suppose he was serious, but it was surely a little mad to think that I would swim across, even downstream, in such circumstances. Nevertheless it seemed polite to ask why.

'Why? Because they steer with their tails. Swimming downstream may give them added speed, but there's considerable loss in the accuracy of their navigation – and *that's* what would be a good thing from your point of view. You'd have much less chance if they were coming for you upstream.'

'I see,' I said.

He grinned and offered me another cigarette. Tea came in on a tray, the telephone came in again on its cable, an ibex came to the door on a chain with a man hanging on grimly to the other end. Pir sain waved them all away except the tea.

'Now tell me what you really want to know,' he said, in a new voice.

* * *

There was so much that I wanted to know – about his father, the hanged Pir, for example: and whether there had been another side to the demoniac personality he had presented throughout his life to history and the British. About this young man himself with his English background, and about how it had felt to be suddenly and quite unexpectedly God. I wanted to ask about the man called Rahim Hangaro – a Hur in the darkest tradition who in the years immediately before the new Pir's accession in 1952, had been terrorising the countryside. The throne of the Pagaros had been empty then, the Hurs had no God: the evil and the good were uncontrolled and free-floating: but in 1952, Hangaro must have sniffed the air and sensed the changes that the new Pir's rule would bring with it, sensed them and turned his face aside. He had withheld his allegiance from Pagaro. The new Pir was young and inexperienced still and for the first time he now tested the power that had descended upon him, pronouncing the formula of excommunication from the Hur brotherhood that would drive Hangaro 'out into the desert to die as a jackal dies'. The spell had worked. Within thirty-six hours, Hangaro and his bandits had been rounded up and delivered over to justice – by the very people who had hitherto been too terrified even to give evidence against him – Hangaro whose amusement it had been to stand men up in file before him and to see how many he could kill with a single bullet. He hoped one day to bring down ten, or so he had said, and people claimed that already he had managed nine. But the young Pir was on the throne now and the words that he had spoken had been enough to encompass Hangaro's downfall. And there had been no Hur outrages ever since. It was very strange.

I wanted to ask about Power – that heady, corrupting stuff: about Absolute Power, and how on earth this young man, while trying to exercise it for good, could hope to escape from the Absolute Corruption of it. I wanted to ask about the *Farqi* Hurs, and whether it was really proving possible for him to redeem them and yet to retain their allegiance to the Pir: for to redeem his Hurs must surely mean to undermine the sources of his power over them. But the conversation attached itself to little, isolated facts instead.

What was I told that evening? That the Hurs are divided into twelve *sangats*, or branches: ten are *Salimi* and two *Farqi*. Pir sain has one hundred and twelve *khalifas*. A new *murid*, whether *Farqi* or *Salimi*, must be proposed by responsible members of the *sangat* to which he seeks admittance, and an assembly must sit to consider his application. Even Pir sain's claim to the empty throne of Pir-jo-Goth in 1952 had had to be submitted to a formal assembly of the Hurs and of the representatives of the direct dynastic line from the first Pir Pagaro. On ascending the throne, the name that Pir sain's father had given him was ritually changed to a dynastic name – Shah-i-Mardan. Each *sangat* must provide a body of men for service in the mosque and shrine – to keep the place swept and clean and cared for, and this each of the twelve *sangats* would do in rotation for one month in the year. What else?

'I have not been able to make a tour of my people in India since I succeeded to the *gadi*,' Pir sain told me. 'It would be politically unwise. Incidentally I have at least as many *murids* over the borders in India as I have here in Pakistan, you know.'

'How many have you in all, then, Pir sain?' I asked him.

I really don't know who estimated what, that evening. Could there be as many as eight hundred thousand, and of that total about one hundred and fifty thousand *Farqis*? Someone in the party blandly doubled these figures. I remembered having heard people in Karachi estimate a total of half a million.

'I shan't rebuild the "kot," Pir sain was saying – and this was as near as he got to speaking of his father on whose account the British had destroyed it. 'In any case not yet awhile. Times have changed. I think perhaps the thing to do is to build myself a house in Karachi. Now that I've had two years on the *gadi*, more than two years, and have settled in, my Hurs begin to understand how I propose that things shall be. I hope to be able to devote much more of my time to politics, in future. There's so much to be done in Sind. A man in my particular position ought to be able to do something. At least I hope so.'

The men sitting on the floor had started to sway a little. They were tired. One of them yawned. From the mosque nearby we could hear the call of the muezzin – the fifth and last call to prayer of the day. The men made little hieratic movements with their hands in token of their good intentions. Pir sain went on talking. Perhaps he had not heard the muezzin.

'Come to breakfast with me tomorrow,' he said. 'I'll send for you.'

* * *

The otaq which had seemed so dingy (let's be honest), so dismal, so empty and discomforting during the hours that I had waited for the King of Kings to summon me, was quite different (or seemed so) when I returned from my first audience. To begin with it was now filled with people: all smiling – I think because the news of my kindly reception must have come back to them over the grapevine quicker than I had been able to do so myself on my own feet. I looked round me: the faces were lit with a new light; or perhaps it was I who had been transfigured for them, so that I was acceptable now, no longer the gloomy, bored and boresome creature in a formal suit. Had I been worked upon by Pir sain's grace? Had an effulgence been set about us all? If so, then this effulgence, and the sun-yellow sheets on my bed with their patterning of Persian cones, and the quilt of rayon satin (turquoise one side and a mulberry-red the other) – these things together had produced a glow that put the 15-watt lamp to shame in its corner.

Pagāro – II

The men came into my room in ones and twos and squatted, and very soon there were eight of them with me. Whatever the position of each in the Pir-jo-Goth hierarchy, I was at least sure of this: that none of the men here with me was a *Farqi* Hur. Gunga the deaf-mute proceeded to introduce them to me.

He mimed a tray – a butler's tray with its load of little and big vessels. A man bowed and laughed and gave his name: 'Sachal.' Next, a dishcloth and a dirty dish: 'Sājan.' Next something that I could not identify but the others laughed, knowing what it was: I still don't know, but the man said his name was Săjan. Next, a steering-wheel and a wad of chewing-tobacco between the cheek and gums: 'Akbar Khan': the man bowed as he said it, an obvious Afridi Pathan. I whispered something to him in Pashto and he replied, smiling as he came over to squat beside me. Pathans like the privacy of their own language. Then there was someone who said he was 'Bombaywala Pahliwan' – the Wrestler from Bombay. Gunga presented him in a crouching posture, with cheeks blown out to balloons and little eyes flashing. Then, before the pantomime was finished, Majna came in.

Here in the otaq, where he had no specific purpose and perhaps no right to be, Majna was at a disadvantage. Outside, the others had seemed scared of him, but here, on their own ground, they took him and pushed him back towards the door and Majna cried out furiously to me to stop them.

'Let him come in!' I shouted.

They dropped their hands and Majna strode in, frowning round at them. He crossed to the bed that I was reclining on, beginning his speech as he came over.

'It is being said of me that I have mistreated you and put my hands upon you, but it is not true!'

I thought of the little scene outside the mosque so short a while before, but I said: 'No. It is not true. You were kind enough to lend me your handkerchief – that's all.' And then I suddenly remembered that I had left the handkerchief in Pir sain's room, folded and laid across the arm of the sofa. 'But I have left it in the "kot"!' I exclaimed.

135

'The handkerchief is not important now,' Majna said. 'But they are saying, all of them, that I have mistreated you – and this is what they have dared to tell our Lord – these people who are outside the Truth! But I have *not* mistreated you!'

'No, of course not,' I said. 'Not in the very least.'

He glared round at the others. 'Of course, I have not! This sain and I are friends. We went walking together. Didn't we?' he demanded of me.

'Yes, we did.'

'Just as I was saying.' He put his hand into his shirt and withdrew a half-packet of cigarettes. 'These are for you.'

Things of this sort, the symbols of giving and forgiveness, must not be refused. I said: 'Thank you,' and held out the packet to him to take one.

He did not even bother to say no. 'They are *all* for you and for *no* other man. I am leaving now.' He stalked to the door but turned as he reached it. 'Tomorrow you are to tell our Lord what you have now told me before these people,' he said. And then he left us.

We were silent for a while after his going. He had disturbed the air. But soon Sājan (or was it Săjan or Sachal – I cannot pretend now to be certain which) sang for us, and some of the others drummed an accompaniment with their fingers on whatever resonant thing lay handy. The Wrestler from Bombay left us. We could hear him intoning his prayers in the next room. Akbar Khan the Afridi got up to fetch my travelling rug and wrapped himself in it. It was cold now and I pulled the quilt over me. Gunga the deaf-mute, who had lost his audience on Majna's appearance, managed to regain it momentarily, though only at the cost of having to make his own exit.

'I go to relieve myself!' he mimed, preposterously obscene: and then, for climax, he exploded his lips in the triumphant Call of Nature.

* * *

Pagāro – II

Breakfast with Pir sain next morning was an immense meal: omelettes; aubergines stuffed and accompanied by a delicious curry sauce; rice; roast hog-deer; chapattis; sweets, *halwas*, fruit: the whole thing washed down with *lassi*, a drink composed of curds, sugared and laced with pounded pistachios or other nuts. Finally coffee was served in little cups and we sat round for a while, sipping it and talking.

I glanced round the room, hoping to see Majna's handkerchief which would have given me the perfect lead-in to the matter of which he had spoken the night before, but it was nowhere visible. I therefore had to remind Pir sain of its existence in order to say my piece. He was very offhand about it, waving the silly little incident aside, and when I tried to lead the conversation from Majna to the *Farqi* Hurs and the problems they must still represent, he diverted it to politics in a more general sense – as if I would agree with him that Hurs as electors were more interesting than Hurs as men.

None of Pir sain's personal entourage could be a *Farqi* Hur: that much went without saying. Pagaro was still God for his *Farqis*, and God must remain the Unapproachable, even if he is present and visible and well-intentioned. His personal circle of intimates are *non-Farqis*, and I felt that even if the *Farqis* were learning to curb their traditional hatred and jealousy of such privileged outsiders, the lesson could not yet be fully learnt.

It is not an easy inheritance that falls to Pagaro: to be God for his Hurs, to do wrong or right in his all-seeing wisdom, to talk carelessly (as men inevitably do sometimes) and to remember too late that his words are magical and sacrosanct. I had been wondering what characteristics in a man could save him from perdition, if he were called upon to be Pagaro. Imagination, certainly – but not too keen: an intellect, but not too rare. Humanity and kindliness. A sense of duty and of humour, and a capacity to see that his own person is as ridiculous as that of other men – almost. To escape damnation Pir Pagaro must be solid and good in the simplest ways. One of Pir sain's uncles, Pir 'Ali Muhammad Rashidi (the friend who had arranged this visit to Pir-jo-Goth for me) had spoken of this too. 'Ali Muhammad is a highly intelligent man, with a darting, inquisitive mind. He is a voracious reader in several languages, and a strong individualist. He had said to me: 'To be Pagaro? Hm-m ... You know, I believe that I would find the synthesis between the intellect and the emotions impossibly difficult to maintain. I doubt if I could have managed it, if I had been called upon to be Pagaro.' I knew what he must mean. What were needed were the calmer, solider, less brilliant virtues. 'Ali Muhammad felt that his young relative, Pir Shah-i-Mardan Shah the Second, was proving to be the right man, and so far as I was able to observe and understand for myself, I agreed with him. In reviving the Pagaro throne and in freeing the Hurs, the Pakistanis had taken a grave risk – but it had been a calculated risk and it looked as if their calculations had been accurate.

Our stomachs were full. It was time to relax. I can hardly blame Pir Pagaro for not wanting to talk about the Hurs. He led me out into the gardens with two or three of his companions. We stood there with the modest little encampment all around us – the hut we had fed in, the tent he slept in, the little cottage that presumably concealed his wife.

* * *

Back in the otaq a man came in: Fulano. He had been with us the night before.

'The day is beautiful,' he remarked, gesturing at it through the door.

'Yes.'

'It is the very best day for visiting Sukkur. That fine city, so near. Only twenty miles, or ten.'

'So little?'

'Less, even.'

'Are you going there, then? Is there a bus?'

'No. There is no bus: but if Pir sain knew that you were so yearning to visit Sukkur today, he would at once offer a car and a driver to drive the car.'

Pagāro – II

'I see,' I said. 'But I have visited Sukkur before, several times, and I shall be going there again perhaps when I leave Pir-jo-Goth, *Insha' Allah*, so it seems rather silly to put Pir sain to so much trouble.'

'But it is no trouble at all, not at all any trouble for Pir sain to offer you the car! He has but to order it and it is done. And there is nothing for you to do, here in Pir-jo-Goth.'

In a way it was true. I did not care about shooting, and it was already only too evident that I was to be shielded from the *Farqi Hurs*. They were coming to heel, perhaps, but it might take a little more time yet: and meanwhile outsiders would be kept from them. It crossed my mind that possibly Sukkur …

'You should say that you wish to go to Sukkur *now*,' said Fulano, looking at his watch. He had been observing me and had clearly sensed a weakening in my resolve. '*Now*,' he repeated, 'and to return in the evening.' He beckoned to Gunga the deaf-mute who had been hovering about at the door, and explained the project to him in mime: steering wheels again, and something else, with a scalloped edge, a series of little semicircles bouncing along in the air about waist-high – or would it be a caterpillar? I didn't follow his meaning for a few moments but Gunga did, immediately, and caught at my hand, laying it to his cheek in that odd gesture he has to indicate delight. Then I saw it too: of course – Sukkur Barrage with its mile-long masonry caterpillar of a barrage over the Indus.

'And I will drive!' signalled Gunga.

'But has he a driving licence, Fulano?'

Fulano made him show me his licence, a perfectly authentic document entitling him to drive a variety of vehicles, including steamrollers, oddly enough. Yet, after all, perhaps neither Sukkur, nor Gunga as driver, was a very good idea. I said so.

They both looked crestfallen. Something else lay behind this outing, naturally. I decided to test them.

'If I went to Sukkur, Fulano, would you come too?'

'If you ordered me, sain.'

'And what would you do if you came to Sukkur with me?'

'I would look after you and serve you.'

'I see.'

I did indeed see this much. But if *I* were to go to Sukkur – *if* I were to go – it would be wonderful to be alone for a little. Never to be alone for an instant throughout the day, and to be closely guarded by watchmen hoicking and spitting throughout the night: these kindlinesses are hard to escape from.

'And if,' I resumed, 'I *ordered* you to leave me when we reached Sukkur, and to rejoin me two or three hours later, what would you do?'

'I would do as you ordered, sain, and I would rejoin you after two or three hours.' Fulano's voice was meek and respectful and he caught Gunga's eye as he spoke. But Gunga had not heard the speech and now begged Fulano to explain. This was no moment for miming the progress of a plot, however, and Fulano looked down at his stomach demurely. I allowed a few seconds to pass while I savoured my counterplot, and then said, pointedly:

'And would two or three hours be enough for you, Fulano?'

'Yes,' he answered, without looking at me. 'If it would be enough for you, sain, of course it would be enough for me, for who am I but your servant?'

I think we felt now that honour had been preserved on both sides, so – to please us all (for our different reasons) – I went to ask Pir sain if he could spare a car and a driver so that I might visit Sukkur. He agreed at once.

'Gunga says he would like to come too, Pir sain.'

'Gunga? You know, of course, that I don't allow him to drive. Oh yes, he's got a licence: but he is never allowed to drive. Poor Gunga. You've seen how it is, and it isn't only his deafness. He would be much too dangerous. I let him maoeuvre the cars in and out of the garages, that's all. But he was so unhappy because he had no licence that I fixed it for him. He is very proud of it, isn't he? And after all life doesn't offer him very much.'

* * *

Pagāro – II

So we went to Sukkur.

The car was a magnificent jukebox, with winking eyes and a chromium-plated smile and very, very large. It was just as well that it should be so large because, apart from myself – for whom a small corner was reserved in the back – there were seven other passengers and the driver. The driver was not Gunga. We closed all the windows against the dust and bounded along a track that followed the banks of a canal, more or less safe, more or less clean, in our hermetically sealed container.

'Drive into the centre of the town,' I told the driver as we approached Sukkur. 'You can leave me there, and pick me up again in three hours.'

My companions exchanged comfortable glances. We were all very pleased with ourselves.

It was wonderful to be alone for a little, and nonetheless alone because Sukkur seethed with people. It is a remarkably untidy town: everything overflows from the bazaar booths into the streets: merchandise, rubbish, men, animals. People take their ease wherever they find it, and they are unexacting. Cafés, kerbstones, gutters. Men with electroplated cruet stands wander about, seeking custom – '*Champi! Champi!*' – massage, the kneading and gentle pressing of limbs, the oiling, the shampooing of the hair, the thick, black, lustrous Sindi hair, the tending of the beards, all in the open street. I drank some coffee: I walked a little: I examined the 'stills' in the entrance to a cinema. They were showing a 'Western' that day: an 'Eastern-Western', as a matter of fact, produced in India with Indian cowboys and bandits. The leader of the bandits was a lady: she looked very beautiful and brave in the 'stills', but it occurred to me that swelling thighs are fine in their place and hell in riding breeches and you cannot have it both ways. She had a pistol in a holster and a great coiled whip in her hand. Whom would she be shooting and thrashing? The men with big moustaches and love-lorn eyes in some of the other 'stalls'? Probably. And then in the last reel love would come into her heart and thaw it, and off would come her breeches and on would go a sari or something loose and she would sing a song for twenty minutes by the clock. This would be the last of many twenty-minute songs. I did not go in. Instead I climbed out of the centre of the town to the plateau that stands above it, up between the eroded crumbling cliffs that flank the road. There is a shrine perched on the top with a ninety-foot tower, a minaret in red brick. It was built in the early seventeenth century, slightly (but not uncomfortably) out of the perpendicular. They call it Masum's Tower. I climbed its winding staircase.

It was consoling to be alone at the top of Masum's Tower, in the little iron cage that prevents you from flying out. The birds of the air – parakeets and kites and others – circle about and look at you through the bars, shrieking with laughter. The floor of the cage is of limestone worn smooth and marmorine by the behinds of the thousands who have sat there being mocked at by birds. But it is peaceful and safe. Down the cliff to one side the town sprawls haphazardly. To the east is the Indus, quite close, though sluggish at this season, with the island of Shri Sadbhela Tirath floating on it. This island is covered with trees and buildings in the manner of an Indian teashop fresco or Douanier Rousseau. It was the home, before partition, of Udiasin Sannyasis, Hindu mystics, and their Lord was His Holiness Shri 108 Swami Harnandasji. I have sometimes wondered what the 108 could mean. Would it be the one hundred and eighth in the succession of Holinesses Shri …? If so, the vista of Holinesses would make the seven Pagaros look a bit silly. Or would it be a magic number, like the 1¼ that recurs all over the place in the Hindu world; '1¼ true is the deity Shri.' What could that mean? Sir Richard Burton comments on this, wondering what it might represent: and I shall add to the confusion by bringing in His Highness the Maharajah of Jaipur whose name is Sawai Man Singh – 1¼ Man Singh. He flies a minute pennant as symbol of it under his house flag. But what does it mean?

I was in no mood for mystical arithmetic. I wanted only to sit and let the birds of the air wheel and whirl and shriek at me through the bars. It was good to be alone, and bad to hear the shuffling of feet on the spiral staircase leading up to my ninety-foot eyrie. Two

Pagāro – II

men emerged through the little arch, bowing to avoid striking their heads against the masonry. They sat down in the cage – very close to me, because the cage cannot hold more than three or four people at a time.

They puffed in silence for a bit. The climb up is very steep. I was resentful of them and didn't look their way. After a little one of them spoke.

'He will not return of his own will because he is *shalkhai*,' the voice said in Pashto, firm and resonant.

I changed my position, trying to make it seem as if I were merely easing my legs. I could now see the two men without having to turn my head. *Shalkhai*. A peculiar word to use of a man. It means a 'blank cartridge' in Pashto.

'I tell you he will not return to us because he is *shalkhai*,' the speaker said again, still more authoritatively. He was tall and fortyish, with a fine head under the conical cap and the very disreputable turban wound about it. Tidy men rewind their turbans often. This was not a very tidy man, and his turban badly needed redoing. He had an old coat and baggy khaki pantaloons in the Pathan manner and a military greatcoat round his shoulders, very tattered. Talismans were pinned here and there about his person. Excellent teeth, very white and regular, a spade beard, very black, and eyes that rested tranquilly in their casings. The second man was very much younger than the first and was speaking now:

'But yes, he will return to us, Kaka sahib. You will see.'

'But no, he will not return to us, Muhammad Khan, because he is *shalkhai*.' This was the first man again and I should explain that 'Kaka' is paternal uncle in Pakistan, just as 'Mania' is maternal uncle, though strangers to the country would never guess. Kaka sahib did not seem to be very disturbed by the fact that 'he' – whoever he was – would not return: he was righteously angry rather than disturbed, I would have said. But the younger man in the old frayed shirt and a sort of shawl thrown round him was much put out.

'But if he does not return to us, Kaka sahib, then who will do the good cooking?'

Kaka sahib swung slowly round upon the young man and said: '*You* will do the good cooking, Muhammad Khan.'

'I? But, Kaka sahib, Pir sahib! I am unable!'

'And what is this that you keep saying with your little mouth – that you cannot do the good cooking? Can you not learn? You are young.'

Muhammad Khan said sadly: 'Oh Kaka sahib, I can perhaps learn, if there should be a master-cook to teach me, and if God wills.'

'The *shalkhai*-one is down there!' announced Kaka sahib, ignoring the young man's bleatings and pointing out through the bars of our cage, out over the higgledy-piggledy untidiness of Sukkur City. 'There! I know it! You see the clocktower?'

Both Muhammad Khan and I looked where he was pointing. There were dozens of clocktowers, or so it seemed, but I took him to be referring to a big, turn-of-the-century, Gothic-revival tower with Indo-Saracenic exfoliations, about two hundred yards diagonally below us. 'Very well. Follow the eye beyond it,' continued Kaka sahib, and we hung upon his words: 'You see that building with the three, the four storeys? Over behind *there* is where the creature hides himself – in the *chakla*! I know it.'

And over behind there, too, in the *chakla*, was where *they* hid themselves, my own companions – I knew it: for the *chakla* is the quarter reserved for the public ladies of a city (and in Sukkur there are a great many such ladies) and these ladies would already be sitting out on their balconies, half-screened, prinking themselves against the joys and torments of the afternoon session. Or perhaps it was already over…?

I looked again at the clocktower. Was it really three hours since I had parted from them in the marketplace? I got up creakingly and stretched my legs.

'Good be on your way,' I said to the two men in Pashto and they looked at me in surprise, as if they had not even noticed my presence until the moment of my leaving.

* * *

Masum's Tower had grown smaller and smaller and had finally slipped behind a little tree and was seen no more. Then the river had slipped behind its banks, and the canal, after remaining as constant as telegraph wire for miles, had swung away, had wheeled away and disappeared – but to counterbalance all this, the citadel of Pir-jo-Goth grew bigger and solider in the landscape and before long we were drawing up under its walls. We stayed in the car with the windows closed for some moments while our dust-cloud overtook us and passed on, and I watched it spread forward soft and noiseless and slither out like surf through which servants came paddling to welcome our return. I did not see Pir sain that evening, but had dinner in the otaq and went early to bed.

I lay in bed thinking for a long time and then suddenly they must have switched off the donkey engine, because the little bulb low down in the corner near the door went off and the world was plunged into darkness. Soon after, a door started to bang itself shut and open and shut again in the still black air. I lay listening to this for a bit and then got out of bed wrapped in the quilt of turquoise and mulberry-red rayon to look for the door and bolt it shut, but it was not in the room next to mine, nor in the room beyond that, and finally I decided to let it alone to work out its own miserable little salvation with no push from me – for who was I to push it? Who *was* pushing it, moreover? *Clack! Bong!* A poltergeist? The idea had come to me a little while before and I had smiled in the darkness, but I was less ready to smile now, and suddenly I asked myself what I supposed I was doing here, wrapped in a quilt all coloured like the night – and what was I doing in the wider sense, deep in the valley of the Indus, trotting around after saints and dervishes, from pillar to post, from pir to poltergeist – and was it truly a door in the far room, swinging itself open clack! and closed bong! while I stood waiting? clack! – bong! I groped my way back to bed and lay there silent in the noisy dark.

Nothing stirs in Pir-jo-Goth but it is stirred by Pir sain, and in the course of that night Pir sain had left us in order to shoot crocodiles, and in the morning a big, grey pall seemed to hang over everything. Time, I supposed. Time unstirring. There was enough of it in all conscience, and nothing at all to be done with it except sit still and hope that it might pass, like clouds. I went to the shrine and sat there, but something had happened since my visit eight years earlier. It looked the same – tombs, and an empty space for more, the dome above them – but it was changed, perceptibly. Something had gone, or rather something was going out of the place.

Sitting there uncertainly with a handkerchief over my head I told myself that the magic was slowly seeping away, so slowly that you could wait a week or a month and be unaware of change. I remembered how it had filled the shrine like an interdiction when first I had been here – but it had been different then: there was no Pagaro. Later, when the Seventh Pagaro arose to give the Hur world meaning once again the magic must have wrapped itself about him, an emanation of the Hurs themselves. They existed through their pir, and he through them, by virtue of the powers with which they could invest him. But his powers depended upon his being God; and if he should deliberately deny his godhead, the magic or whatever it was would have nothing left to feed on, and would die. Already it must be sinking, it seemed to me. When the process was complete, the *Farqi* Hurs, those 'separate and holy' people, would have become once more the peasants from whom their forerunners had sprung – decent, God-fearing, pir-respecting peasants. It would be better so, even if there should remain some who would echo the Hur lament of the time when first the British rounded them up and held them in closed settlements.

'The country looks now without its charms: everything looks barren, the pleasant *Farqis* are gone, and without them we all are nothing more than birds without feathers.' I wandered out of the shrine through the side door with the heavy woollen fringe and the cowrie shells, through the mosque itself and into the court. Under the trees a boy was holding a gazelle on a cord. Pigeons perched in line over above the gateway to the inner citadel. Men slumped at the gate, waiting. Perhaps I should go now.

Pagāro – II

I had meant to move on to a place farther down the valley, to the *gadi-nisshin* of another well-known shrine, but I had begun to wonder ... Had I set about things all wrong from the start? Might it not be that even to have contemplated such a journey was, for me, hopeless?

What had I hoped for, anyway? The concept of hereditary, living saints was not new to me. I had been familiar with it for years. I knew the words, too – anyone can learn them if he cares to: but to experience directly what the words stood for was a different matter, and I had wanted to know. Once or twice I had had what had seemed for a moment to be the beginnings of comprehension – sitting in a shrine, for instance, as at Sehwan, or here in Pir-jo-Goth. And years before in the presence of a man in the Chitral valley and in the presence of the same man again, later, under the chinar trees of Kashmir, I had understood (or thought I understood) without having to consider the question at all, that this would have been the pir for me if I had been a Muslim in search of a pir. But I was not a Muslim in search of a pir and I must remain outside when it came to the point. The initiates of Sehwan and of Pir-jo-Goth excluded me. Probably they divined that I lacked faith in their symbols.

Hereditary saints are symbols for something else, after all, and they are like talismans against the evils that beset the weak and ignorant. A man can make an act of resignation and give his pir power over him, or else he can bow in a formal sort of manner and put something into the collection plate without resigning any part of himself – much as some people in Christendom go to church because it is a respectable habit to have formed. Or, if a man has studied, he could dress his pir up in metaphysics and observe him from the outside – objectively – though this would not take him very far upon the Way. But whatever his attitude it would be worthless for him to note only that the little blue stone of the talisman was not a turquoise but just a little blue stone of no value. The inner truth, whatever it may be, persists, even if one tells oneself that the pirs are for the most part perfectly ordinary, rather self-indulgent men with a foothold to establish in the heart and a living to make. Where it all leads must depend not upon the pir, but upon oneself: if there is faith in a man's heart he may find tranquillity. If he has insufficient faith, then of course it will lead him nowhere.

6
A Frieze of Dervishes

THE NEXT DAY I LEFT PIR-JO-GOTH, and the next night I passed in the searing cold of a waiting-room, a rug and a disgraceful old duffle-coat over me. Trains went pounding by down below in the darkness and between trains a little engine that sounded squat and square chugged about the station yard and whistled fit to burst.

Discomfort is of various orders, and life is hedged about with it. We say 'Such is Life' sententiously, and we sigh; but most people don't complain so long as there are compensations and so long as the goodish or the good outweighs the bad. But nothing, nothing, can compensate for the dingy discomfort of waiting-rooms and of railway canteens, nothing can compensate for tea at times like steam and at times like flat boiled water, nor for flies that whirr in on the wings that God has given them, to take refuge with us from the heat of summer and from the withering cold of winter. A waiting-room waiting for the dawn and hung with coloured exhortations ... come to Lahore! – come to Murree! – to Quetta! – Mohenjo-daro! – to this, to that! – and I had come to this, to Rohri Junction.

The dawn came, nevertheless, and life seeped back into the extremities. A waiting-room attendant, gaunt and bearded, peeped in at the door, his blue redingote trailing to his knees. He would be as bony as a fish under his coverings, but he was quiet and kind. Without any asking he brought me a mug of steam-tea from the canteen below, and then began talking of life and misery, but in the most respectful manner, using the honorific '*Huzoor*' which means something like 'Presence' and demands a verb in the third person plural. *Huzoor* is thus superior, in my view, to the various European-language honorifics we have heard of – *majesté* and *altesse*, the Spanish *Usted*, the Italian *Lei* – which dare not ask for more than a third person singular, and are feminine at that: and though it is true that a European king may speak of himself as 'we', we do not speak of him as them – so it can at once be seen how honouring it is to be addressed as '*Huzoor*', and for this reason I did what I could to drink the steam-tea though I would rather have shaved in it.

I shaved in cold water, brushed my teeth, and squatted with the soap under the tap in the washhouse and came out to find that the sun was up meanwhile – and when the winter sun comes up over the Indus Valley the whole world changes to a cradling yellowness, a splendour warm and basking, with the sky a water-blue and only wisps of the most distant cloud afloat in it. I came out onto the verandah and into this renewed and lovely world.

The waiting-room at Rohri Junction is housed on the first floor of a sad two-storeyed building, with the restaurant-cum-canteen below it. It is quite separate from the main body of the station with the platforms and ticket offices and the intermittent raging of the trains. It stands on its own tumulus and a wide verandah fronts it. From this verandah you can ignore the signal boxes and the boring parallels of the permanent way, and look instead towards the town itself – for the town of Rohri enjoys its own personal life and death, having nothing to do with the station that has snatched its name, and nothing at all to do with the traffic that roars by on the railway lines. No one is likely to get out of the train at Rohri except to change trains for somewhere else.

'Can I leave my luggage here in your charge?' I asked the attendant. 'I'm going for a walk.'

'The luggage will be safe, *Huzoor*. What train will it be?'

'No train.'

'Then? It is for some inspection, this visit? To see something?'

'See something? What, for instance?'

'Well, anything the *Huzoor* might wish to see. The Barrage. The Biscuit Factory.'

A Frieze of Dervishes

I had seen the barrage time and time again, and I was too old to be excited by biscuits. So I said: 'No.'

He looked at me incredulously. What could this Englishman be doing here, then? Why? Whither? 'To Rohri just for walking ...?' he whispered.

I refused to answer such a question, refused even to ask it of myself. Yet the man looked so dismayed that I felt I must say something:

'I shall look at the suspension-bridge,' I said, and this seemed to solace him. And indeed why not the suspension-bridge, if it came to that?

I wandered away along the railway embankment that curves round in the direction of the river.

Over on Rohri's flanks citizens were answering the calls of nature but being careful to avoid the tombstones that abound. It is a goblin panorama that spreads across the foreground – ridges and tumuli and eroded chasms, flint and limestone, shrines, tombs, tomblets, here and there small groups of dusty trees and dusty goats, and the town itself staggering like an exhausted man behind it all. It is an ancient town. Many of the older buildings are of mud slapped onto a skeleton of wooden members. Eventually the mud falls away like flesh from wooden bones and then you can see these old houses propped against the skyline with the heavens showing through their ribs.

I walked on in the curve of the embankment, the bridge ahead, the river down below – and here the vagaries of the shoals and currents have cut a deep bay into Rohri's river-face, so that the town could almost be said to possess a bathing beach. It was from this beach that the tonga-ponies were taking a bath that morning, I remember, in the shadow of the bridge. Their owners were sluicing them with water and they stood hock-deep and enraptured.

I walked on slowly over the bridge on the narrow footpath that accompanies the track, hoping that a train would rumble by, and ten minutes later I was on the right bank of the Indus, in the high-lying northern sector of Sukkur where the district administrative buildings have all been grouped. I walked past a man selling flutes and another man buying one, past a garden filled with peepul trees and the mushroom-coloured shadows that lay under them, past whitewashed, shuttered bungalows that looked as if they might be empty but for the white ants, past a little ridge that supports the Collector of Sukkur's secretariat, then in the lea of another that supports a public garden where nothing seems to grow except a clocktower dedicated to a bygone Literacy Campaign – but none of these things was capable of holding my attention because already a little way ahead, on the crest of what I knew would be the cliff overlooking the old city, Masum's Tower reared up into the sunshine – and if the waiting-room attendant had been present now to ask his question – where? and what? – I would have been able to reply with calm and certainty: 'To sit in Masum's Tower.'

It is high, but not too high: high enough to soothe the spirit, yet not so high that the details of life moving down below become incomprehensible – the details, for example, of the people on the terrace at the foot of the tower, just outside the walls of the shrine to which the tower belongs. People like to walk about and sit on this terrace in the winter sun. The road to the city curls round it and down, driving in a steep diagonal under a limestone cliff-face and then flattening out as it reaches the main market square with its seething but slow-motion traffic.

The hoot of motor horns comes softly up to Masum's Tower – but I paid as little heed to them as do the bullock carts or bicycles or men at whom they hoot. I felt at peace. Below me on one of the benches set along the length of the terrace was an old man making a patchwork coat out of diamond-shaped patches that a child was busy cutting out beside him. It would be a month-long occupation and would certainly entail foraging for more patch-cloth than they had managed to collect together yet: but the child was absorbed with its scissors, and the old man looked happy in the sunshine, and every now and then he would lay the patching flat across his knee and smooth it lovingly. On a bench nearby a youth was massaging his companion's shoulder, and though I heard no sound I could see from the sudden movement the shoulder made each time the

A Frieze of Dervishes

youth bore down upon it, that the massaged man must be grunting with pain. There was something familiar about the man – maybe the tattered greatcoat of military cut that he had half-slipped from his shoulders so that his companion could do the massage properly. After a bit I realised that they were probably the two men who had clambered up into Masum's cage that day – two days, three days ago now? – and I remembered the older one's name: Kaka sahib. He was a Syed, evidently, for the younger one had addressed him also as Pir sahib. I remembered some part of their talk, too, and wondered vaguely if they had yet found the runaway, whoever he may have been – the 'blank cartridge'.

I was in no hurry to move.

I could see the whole of Sukkur city now, a diorama not quite real (nothing seemed quite real today) and a couple of miles away the Sukkur Barrage, and of course the Indus with its islands – though the little island to which the Palla fish from downstream used to come to make their reverences to Khwajo Khizr was hidden by a hillock and a group of mainland trees. Khwajo Khizr is god of seas and rivers, and he has an island shrine here. It was the habit of the Palla fish to come swimming up to the island, to bow, to receive the blessings of god, and to retire from his presence backwards, being careful to avoid the disrespect of showing him their tails. But the building of the Sukkur Barrage that has brought so much prosperity to Sind, has put a stop to this pious fish pilgrimage, because the barrage has not been provided with a fish-ladder by which the Palla could climb and complete their journey to the shrine. Probably the Barrage engineers knew that Khwajo Khizr had other shrines farther down the Indus, and assumed that the Palla fish could as conveniently go there instead. Khwajo Khizr has a great many shrines and almost as many names, and his worshippers are not confined to Palla fish. The people of Sukkur and Rohri, for example, honour him constantly with oblations of lamps and sometimes flowers, thinking of him as an old man dressed in green. Thoughts of him are very much in men's minds here.

The man with the hurt shoulder and his companion were still on their bench when finally I came down from the tower, and they were indeed Kaka sahib and his companion, so I greeted them – in Pashto – and asked after their health. But Kaka sahib seemed preoccupied and barely looked up even, and the younger man did not stop his massage, though he answered my greeting quite civilly. So I left them to it, passing on down by the steps that rejoin the road to the city, and I was soon in the city itself.

In a street leading away from the main market square with its clocktower and its girdle of noisy cafés, in a fly-blown but peaceful little side-street I found a café and sat down in it. I chose this particular café, I think, because of an object both strange and charming set up on a table outside it: a little wooden train about nine inches high and perhaps two foot long, all painted in the brightest colours, a locomotive and one truck. On top of the locomotive's chimneystack was perched an enamel basin, and up from the chimneystack, through a hole in the bottom of the enamel basin, was squirting not smoke but water. A ping-pong ball danced at the top of the squirt of water. The purpose of this object was to delight the eye, and so to draw customers to the café – as it had drawn me. All round it were set glasses filled with coloured liquids – pink and purple, green, yellow, red. Several people were sitting in the café drinking one or other of these vivid drinks, though I ordered coffee for myself. I sat there for some time, observing how village people in from the country to the market town were drawn like flies to the little performing locomotive, and how the sophisticated townsfolk could take it all in their stride as if it were quite normal.

Then Kaka sahib and his companion rounded the corner from the market square. They were deep in conversation now and I'm not sure that I would have tried to talk to them again if the younger man had not clutched at Kaka sahib and pointed in my direction, so that Kaka sahib looked too. They came closer and I then realised that it was the performing locomotive that had caught the younger man's eye – but meanwhile Kaka sahib had caught mine.

A Frieze of Dervishes

'Don't get tired,' I said – this being a respectable greeting for Pathans.

'Don't get old,' Kaka sahib responded in a gravely formal voice, this being the correct response to my greeting.

'Come in happiness,' I went on, formal again in my turn.

'Live in happiness …'

I turned to the younger man: 'Come in happiness. Have a "colour".' A 'colour' meant one of the coloured drinks: and he nodded, pointing to the purple as he mumbled his responses: 'And you, Kaka sahib?' I continued. 'Would you like a "colour" too?'

'Me? You know my name?'

'Of course. Don't you want a "colour"?'

'No. But how is it that "of course" you know my name? You are a foreigner: you are not Pathan, you are not even Sindi. You are English, I think. I know the faces that the English people have.'

'I expect everyone knows Kaka sahib by sight, as I do too, though I am English and not from Sind.'

He looked rather pleased at this and said: 'Yes.' But it was obvious that he did not recognise me at all from the previous occasions on which we had seen each other.

'How did you come to hurt your shoulder?' I asked with polite interest, and he at once looked annoyed and started to mutter, so I left him alone for a moment while I ordered a coffee for him although he had refused a drink, and a purple 'colour' for the young man. When he had calmed down a bit, I tried once more – this time with an inquiry after the 'blank cartridge' runaway. 'Have you found the *shalkhai* yet?'

His reaction was explosive anger. 'Stop!' he shouted at me. 'Stop about my shoulder and that poltroon of a *shalkhai*, stop, I tell you!' – and I looked at the other in bewilderment and then back at Kaka sahib who was quiet again and staring studiedly in the opposite direction. When the coffee came and was set before him he pushed it away.

'He is angry,' the young man said, hiding his voice behind his podgy peasant's hand.

'Yes, I can see that. But why?'
'Because of his hurt shoulder and the *shalkhai*.'
'Yes, but ...'
'We should speak of other things ...'
'Very well. What is your name, incidentally?'
'Muhammad Khan.'
'Oh yes, I remember now ...'
'Muhammad Khan!' Kaka sahib had flashed round in his seat at the end of the table and was facing us again, his eyes blazing now. 'Yes, Muhammad Khan is his name, and he fell on it, the fool of fools!'

'Yes, alas, I fell on it,' Muhammad admitted, his head meekly bowed. He was remarkably meek for a Pathan – a simple, good-hearted youth, I judged.

'The fool-boy,' Kaka sahib muttered. 'Stop talking to me of him.'

I was getting annoyed myself by now. How dared Kaka sahib behave in this manner with a stranger! I said: 'I understand nothing, Kaka sahib, except that you are very impolite and not like a Pathan at all. What has taken you, that you behave like this to me?'

'Uh-h?' His voice was suddenly quite small and gentle.

'I don't understand why you are angry with me, nor how it came about that Muhammad fell on "it" – fell on *what*? Your shoulder? How should he fall on it?'

'Yet he did – and I was not angry with you just now, but with Muhammad: and it was because he is sitting beside you that my anger had to pass across you to reach him. *You* should not be angry about this. Anyone can see how it was.'

'And I am not angry about it – I am only bewildered, and I still am unable to understand how Muhammad could have fallen upon your shoulder.'

'What is your name?' he asked patiently.

'Peter.'

He turned to Muhammad and said: 'Tell Peter of your shame and stupidity.'

Muhammad put down his glass of purple drink and hesitated. Then he folded his hands in his lap and looked at them. Finally he

A Frieze of Dervishes

said: 'I was climbing and Kaka sahib was in the street below ...' He hesitated again.

'Go on,' Kaka sahib said. 'Yes. I was quietly waiting in the street below. And then?'

Muhammad sat silent and worried.

'Yes?' I said, to encourage him. 'Go on.'

'And I fell,' he announced flatly.

'On me waiting quietly below. On my shoulder. Now do you understand, Peter?'

'No,' I said. 'I understand "how", of course, but I do not understand "why".'

'Why?' Kaka sahib's voice rose to a shout as he half stood up in his seat, so that this time his anger passed over my head and exploded about Muhammad Khan's. 'Because Muhammad is the fool of fools and he is unable even to climb!'

It had gone on for too long, and all the people in the café were regarding us now, though with a total lack of comprehension. Even if they had understood Pashto, they would still have understood nothing, I imagine – any more than I had. I took Kaka sahib's arm firmly – the arm attached to the sound shoulder – and said: 'If we are to discuss this matter any further, please tell me at once what you were quietly doing in that street, and explain also why Muhammad should be climbing.'

Kaka sahib shook my hand off his arm with a great sweeping gesture. 'And who are *you*, asking all these infant questions? They say the English are rogues, but they do not say anything about the English being fools. We were searching for the *shalkhai* who ran, of course: for Sikunder. I thought you knew. You were asking about him. We were searching for him in his hiding place.'

'At the whorehouse. *Now* do you understand?' demanded Muhammad in a voice modelled on Kaka sahib's, but the latter rounded on him instantly and said: 'It is not for *you* to speak to Peter sahib like that' – and Muhammad looked down sourly at his hands again.

'And what happened next?' I asked.

'Nothing. All that falling had made such a noise in the quiet street – it was nearly dawn, though dark still. And then, you see, there was that terrible pain in my shoulder. We were obliged to leave at once, without even being entirely sure that it was the right whorehouse we were peeping at.' He took a gulp of coffee. 'Now, why do you think that he should have run?' he inquired softly of mid-air. 'It is seven days now, or eight, since he ran ...'

'Is he your servant, Kaka sahib? You didn't beat him, I suppose?'

He looked quickly at me, and then his expression changed to one of disappointment. 'I was not asking you the question, I was asking it of the air. But now I see that after all you do not know me, and that when you said that everyone knows Kaka sahib, even *you* from outside of Sind, you were really only cutting jokes at me.'

'No, no, I wasn't cutting jokes at you!' I exclaimed hurriedly, and with some embarrassment, of course, because in a sense I had been making a joke about how famous he must be, and it was awkward because perhaps Kaka sahib saw himself as a celebrity and wished to be recognised as one – yet with the best will in the world I could not know what he was famous for. So I hummed and ha'd a bit and looked towards Muhammad Khan for help, and he looked very pointedly away.

'Tell him,' Kaka sahib said wearily.

Muhammad swallowed and said, with eyes averted: 'Kaka sahib is our Pir sahib.'

'Tell him better than that.'

'Kaka sahib is our Pir sahib and *gadi-nisshin*.'

'*Gadi-nisshin*? Oh ...?' I had turned towards Kaka sahib and he must have caught the note of special interest in my voice. 'At whose shrine, then?'

'And Muhammad Khan is one of my *murids*,' said Kaka sahib firmly, to close the subject.

'Yes, I see now,' I said. 'And Sikunder is another *murid*, I suppose?'

'Of course. Sikunder is another, and you now see how perfectly necessary it is for me to recover him from among the whores.'

A Frieze of Dervishes

'Oh yes, I can see it all now – moreover I seem to remember that Sikunder is an excellent cook.'

'That too. You knew that? But he is gone, and how am I going to get him back again if he does not wish to come back? Muhammad says he will return, but I say that he will not, so how can we *bring* him out? Muhammad is not large enough. Sikunder is very large.' His voice had been dying away on the last few words and now revived itself, but more as if he were thinking aloud than talking: 'I *wonder*.... If we were to wait some more days – would he then become so weak that even Muhammad could ... or perhaps my shoulder will be well again by then and *I* could ... for I am very strong ...'

Looking at him I could see that he must in fact be very strong, but he was shaking his head sadly and his left hand lay across his right shoulder, pressing and kneading it. 'No, no, it is no good, Peter,' he finished up, addressing me to my face now. 'You can see how sad a pass has been reached. I am wondering now if perhaps the Collector sahib or some other high officer could be told to order that Sikunder be brought back from the *chakla*.' He had become very sad as he mumbled all this, and now he leaned towards me over the corner of the table and said: 'What is your *complete* name?'

'Peter Mayne.'

'Peter Ming?'

'Ming? Mayne. Ming, if you like. But "Peter" is best. Moreover it is a name taken from a great saint.'

'Ah-h! Then I think,' said he, nodding wisely but rather overdoing it: 'Then I think that you are certainly a big officer, in the Irrigation Department perhaps, or else in the Police. Peter Ming sahib, I have something most important to say to you' – and he took my hand between his two, wetted his lips to prepare them for the important speech, and I was too quick for him:

'Alas,' I said firmly, waving negations in the air with my free hand, 'I am neither of the grand things you name, nor anything else at all helpful to the case.'

Hope went draining away from his eyes and then, suddenly, he saw that my hand still lay between his and he put it down quickly on the table again as if it had been something distasteful. 'Never mind,' he said. 'I see that I have made a stupid mistake. I was thinking that you were certainly an important person and would go to some high officer here to request him to take Sikunder out of the whorehouse for me. Yes, at first look I supposed you to be a high officer yourself, even. But now I am looking more closely' – and at this he did look closely at me, at my clothes, at my face, and then away with a slight shiver of the head – 'and I admit my mistake.'

I was not at all pleased, but I tried to hide it. 'Kaka sahib. You know that even the highest officer in the land could not interfere in a matter strictly private. As far as we know your *murid* Sikunder is not committing a technical offence ...' I had difficulty with the Pashto for this, and hesitated. In the short silence Muhammad Khan awoke from a reverie and exclaimed:

'Oh but my God and I am hungry!'

He had been wrapped in his thoughts, and his thoughts had presumably been about food. But we ignored him.

'"Technical offence",' I repeated in English. 'You understand?'

'Of course I understand,' he said truculently. 'Do you not know that I was serving in the Police Department in Punjab for fifteen years before I decided?'

'No.' I was somewhat surprised. 'I hadn't realised that.'

'Oh yes. And it was nice – there in the Police Department. But the officers were all against me always, and I did not get the proper promotions year after year, and I remained a simple constable all because here was I, a Pathan, and there were the others, Punjabis with relatives in important positions to push them up and up and push me down and down. So what fairness could I expect, a Pathan?'

'Come now, Kaka sahib! Be fair yourself!'

'Do not interrupt, please, Peter sahib. Now, for example, I was telling about "technical offence."'

I shouted him down, saying: 'Sikunder is not committing a technical offence. He is doing nothing against the law – so far as we know – and neither are the ladies he is doing it with – and *that* is what I am trying to tell you.'

A Frieze of Dervishes

'Oh but my *God* and I am hungry!' exclaimed Muhammad, rousing himself once more.

'Silence!'

'But aren't you hungry too, Kaka sahib?' I asked him slyly.

'I? I am always hungry, but I do not always speak about it. And in these days it is specially bad because it was Sikunder who was best able to get the food and cook it well for us, and to get the alms – though Muhammad is learning now, and I must not treat him too cruelly, for he is rather new to the Way and the Way is often hard. He suddenly remembered himself and the end in view and said very firmly: 'Do not delude me with food talk, Peter Ming sahib, but tell me instead if you intend to go to the Collector sahib or some other high officer for his assistance, or you do not. Now answer!'

'I have no power to move Collectors.'

'Zzzt!' A jet of spit flew like a hornet across the table and struck a spittoon near the entrance with a tinny clang. 'No *power*! Directly the slightest crumb of favour is asked of you you minge and cringe and say you have no power!'

He stopped at this point, watching my eyes – because as anyone very well knows if he has ever played this tricky game of coaxing and shaming and flattering and humiliating and angering another so that finally he shall be as pulp and do what is required of him, the other's eyes must be watched carefully for his reactions. Consequently Kaka sahib was watching mine and for the same reason I had turned my face away and was regarding the little performing locomotive.

'Nice, isn't it?' I observed to Muhammad Khan. And because good manners required some reply, he replied politely: 'Yes.'

'Silence!' Kaka sahib rapped out, glaring at the young man.

'Midday,' I murmured almost to myself. 'Midday is an inauspicious time to discuss such things, the stomach being empty. I will *not* go for you to the Collector or anyone else, yet I *will* help in the recovering of Sikunder to the extent that I am able, and even if it means pulling him out. We do not know – or in any case we cannot be certain – which side Sikunder will be on in the event of a kidnapping, as you might say, and that makes it even more difficult to discuss sensibly. But anyway this is a bad moment for discussion and an excellent moment for food, and I therefore invite you, Kaka sahib' – I made a little formal bow towards him – 'and your *murid* Muhammad Khan, to take food with me, and by this I mean that I will pay.'

He hesitated – wondering, perhaps, if I had some hidden motive for trying to enslave him with food.

I asked him: 'Do you accept, or not?' – ('... oh we accept, we accept, we accept ...' whispered Muhammad, his eyes closed, 'we accept, we accept ...') 'Do you accept, Kaka sahib?' I demanded.

'We accept,' announced Kaka sahib formally. 'And this matter that we have been discussing can be left aside until we have fed.'

* * *

We ate, the three of us, in a feeding-house close by, and though I cannot say that it was a good meal, yet it was eatable and not unnourishing and it was abundantly clear that neither Kaka sahib nor Muhammad could have eaten much else during the previous twenty-four hours and perhaps for longer.

Kaka sahib released a tremendous and complimentary belch. 'And now,' he said, 'we will go to the kidnapping of Sikunder.'

I said quickly: 'First we must make our plan.'

'Oh yes, we must first make our plan.' He hesitated. 'But what *is* our plan? That is the problem, you see.'

Both Kaka sahib and Muhammad looked at me and I suddenly realised what I had let myself in for. It was I who must plan everything. 'Well,' I began, feeling a little light in the head. I had been feeling a bit light in the head all morning. It was something in the air. I collected my wits together: 'Well, there are various sorts of plan that we could make, but I believe the best in this case would be to get one or two more men to help us: there are many Pathans in this town of Sukkur, as I can see by a simple glance about me, and surely you must know some who are large and look violent, don't you?'

A Frieze of Dervishes

'You mean, Peter, we should hire these people for the kidnapping?'

'Yes, I suppose that's what I *do* mean,' I said, rather surprised at myself. 'If necessary.'

'And the prize-money for these men?'

'Oh, I see. How much do you think they would cost? But haven't you got any Pathan *murids*, Kaka sahib? *Murids* ought to be ready to do it for nothing.'

'As a matter of fact,' Kaka sahib replied, 'I don't happen to have any Pathan *murids* who are both large and violent enough for a kidnapping, except Sikunder himself and he ...'

'... exactly ...'

'... would therefore be no good.'

'Exactly,' I repeated. 'So do you think that five rupees each would be enough prize-money? Two men at five each? I would present the prizes if it were only that much. Or I could go up to rupees seven annas eight each for two men, maximum.'

Kaka sahib looked at me and nodded. 'Five would be quite enough, if it is only necessary to *look* violent, or perhaps with just a little pulling and pushing. But if it comes to blood and beatings, even rupees seven annas eight will be insufficient, I think. What do *you* think?'

'I don't think we ought to have blood and beatings, to tell you the truth, Kaka sahib. And I don't think it will be necessary either, so let us say that five rupees each will suffice.'

'Very well. So now that we have our plan, we have only to find the hired bandits.'

'But don't you see that we haven't yet got a plan at all? We have only decided about the hired men, in case we need help. We still have to consider *how* we are going to do all this. And *when*. Also whether we are to go to the whorehouse pretending to be ordinary decent citizens desiring whores, or what, exactly. I think we should all go to some quiet place now and talk it over carefully.'

'But what is there to talk?' Kaka sahib demanded.

'*One* of us must keep his feet on the ground,' I said, translating a good, solid old British concept which left Kaka sahib unmoved – but which suddenly caused me to realise that my own feet were far from being firmly planted. The whole situation had an edging of fantasy.

'Where do you live, Peter?' he was asking, and this brought me back to earth a little.

'For the moment on a bench in the waiting-room at Rohri Junction.'

'Ah yes, very nice. But they won't let you stay there long, and then only if you buy a railway ticket as if you were going by train somewhere.'

* * *

But as a matter of fact we did not go back to the waiting-room, nor to Kaka sahib's home – wherever that might have been: he said it was a 'kos' distant, which would be about two miles. He had become so excited at the prospect of a kidnapping that he insisted that we walk together through the *chakla* to make a preliminary reconnaissance – which was very sensible, of course.

'Muhammad can go in search of two good and violent men and can bring them to the café where we sat this morning – you understand, Muhammad? The café with the little train and the ball dancing? You and I, Peter, can go walking through the *chakla*, making our plans, and we can seem to be in solemn converse, you see, and it will be almost as if we had strayed into the *chakla* by mistake, you see, thinking it to be the ordinary bazaar: but in fact as we converse I can *secretly* show you the house in which Sikunder hides (or else is being hidden) and I can also show you, in the gully alongside it, the place where Muhammad climbed and fell, the fool-boy, and injured my shoulder.'

'That would be most interesting,' I agreed. 'How does the shoulder feel, by the way?'

'Better but still bad.'

So Muhammad was dispatched to the main market square to watch for likely recruits, and I left a rupee with him with which to feast these men on coffee or 'colour' and hold them there against our return, while Kaka sahib and I strolled nonchalantly away in the direction of the *chakla*.

A Frieze of Dervishes

'It will be like the police days again,' he said happily. 'How shall we begin?'

I thought for a moment. 'If you already know the house and think *they* do not know *you*' – I stopped and corrected myself hastily: 'I mean if you think they know you only as Kaka sahib and *not* as Sikunder's Pir, his *murshid* and spiritual guide, then we can go and sit somewhere near that whorehouse and seem to talk, I suppose, while we look at it and consider. You might perhaps have one of the rents in your greatcoat mended, for instance – if there is a tailor near, and there is sure to be. That would be a wonderful excuse for sitting, wouldn't it? And a wonderful excuse for mending the rents, too.'

'Yes, yes, but first let us walk past once or twice, shall we?'

'I think we would see much more if we were sitting, but never mind: all right, let's go walking past – and I dare say we ourselves could mend *that* big rent here and now by ...'

'Which big rent?' he asked, looking down.

'*That* one ... Simply by holding it together with one of your *tawiz*-pins. The dried eye of the sacrificial sheep has a nice big pin.'

'It isn't really an eye,' he said, fingering it. 'It's just something I found in a café once.'

'Well, it *looks* like an eye.'

'Yes, doesn't it? That's why I like it,' said Kaka sahib, but he did not wish to pin the rent in his greatcoat together with it.

The street was quite wide, and all along it, on both sides, were small shopfronts in which the owners squatted, dispensing their *pan* and *sopari*-nut and the lime that goes with it, or the little local cigarettes called *biris,* or a squirt of violent and passionate perfumes. Then there were several cafés, a tailor shop or two, and a great deal of movement, though this was mostly male. The professional ladies would not walk about the streets, of course – or if they did they would be veiled away from lewd glances. It was not yet three in the afternoon – too early, that is to say, for most of the ladies to be hopeful of custom, but on some of the partly screened balconies at first-floor level we noted signs of life: a woman would come out and yawn, perhaps, and cast a quick glance up and down the street. Below, at street level, there were a good many men with smoky eyes and abstracted expressions – a languor that was belied, however, by the quick furtiveness with which they marked our passage past them. I took them for pimps settling down to business again after the lull of the morning, but they were well-behaved and we were not pestered and one only – a tallish, spare, small-boned Sindi who had a strange mauve dustiness about his skin – even seemed as if he wanted to address us. But he did not and we had passed on. At intervals there were little side alleys, but anyone could see that the smart custom was to be found in this big, main street of the *chakla*.

The women who were coming out onto their balconies at present were mostly the older women, and fat. Perhaps it would be that the not-so-young must put in longer hours of waiting than the little new ones – but against this, as everybody knows, bulky ladies are much in demand in eastern cities, and very young girls are seldom very big in size: so perhaps this counter-weight of nature serves to even out things a little, and gives the older, fat ones an advantage that can outlast youth – a little, anyway. We wandered along the street, deep in conversation. I was asking Kaka sahib about himself.

'You see, my wife had died and she had given me no babies, and there was always this question I have spoken of to you, about no promotion because I was Pathan and everyone else was not, there, in the Punjab, and my officers *all* being against me and ...'

'Come now, Kaka sahib,' I remonstrated, not for the first time in our brief acquaintance.

'Well, there it was, anyhow.' He glanced sideways at me. 'There was this question of no promotion and my wife being dead and no money for another. And then, also, I was frequently thinking about God.' He stopped speaking for a moment and I watched his profile as we walked along together. He was looking calmly ahead, his eyes untroubled. He opened his lips slightly and I saw him bite the tip of his tongue as his eyes screwed up, searching for words to express the memory of that time, perhaps. 'I knew, of course, that

A Frieze of Dervishes

if I could sit and *think* – no, no, not think: I am not clever, to think. My police officers said that I was foolish as an owl, but I didn't care, except that "owl" was a wicked word to use. Well, if I had time just for *sitting*, perhaps I would become fully aware of God and have no more need of promotion, and the peace would come into my heart, and it would be much better than being a policeman – much better than being anything!'

We walked on in silence.

'You are a Syed, of course,' I said.

'Oh yes, I am Syed. But do you think that because I am Syed, a Pir, all I have to do is sit under a tree and the *murids* will flock to me and bring me bread and tea? Well, it is not so at all. They don't.'

Nor indeed had I supposed it to be the case, and I told Kaka sahib so, hoping that this might solace him a little. But we had come out at the end of the street without realising it, and it seemed to me that we should keep our objective in mind.

'I'm afraid we must have passed the house,' I said.

He looked round as if he had forgotten where we were. 'Yes. We must have passed it ... and, oh Peter, do you know! I am entirely uncertain now which *is* the house, even if I see it! I knew before, when we sent Muhammad Khan away to select the assassins – well, not the assassins exactly, but you know what I mean. But I am not at all sure now. Oh what a pity it is! I really don't know what we should do. Shall we walk back along the street again – for I think it must be this street of the *chakla* – and perhaps if we walk back along the other side of the road and look on *this* side, I will recognise the house and the gully beside it where Muhammad fell on my shoulder. The trouble is, you see, Peter, that it is so long since I was a policeman to take notice of such things.' He really was rather upset now, as we walked back together on the other side of the road.

This time several of the girls called down to us softly or less softly from their balconies, or else pimps came up to us and asked if they could be of service, because it seemed evident to them, from the fact of our return, that we were customers – not just citizens walking home through the whores' quarter. Kaka sahib replied to their

167

proposals with the utmost grace, but it in no way helped us to find what we were looking for because he ordained rather quixotically that in speaking with these whores and pimps we should avoid any mention of Sikunder's name, so as to save him from shame – nor did we know of any other name (of a whoremonger, for example, or of one of his ladies) that could help these obliging strangers to help us. So, finally, having walked twice more up, and twice more down the street, I made Kaka sahib stop and said to him:

'Listen to me. We are wasting our time. We had better go back to the café with the performing locomotive and we can sit there, considering our plan, until Muhammad comes. And *he* will know which house it is.'

'Yes, but ... You must remember, Peter, that on no account must we confess to Muhammad that we were unable to find the house – because it would seem like forgetfulness, I mean, and look very bad. After all, I *am* his Pir.'

'No, of course not. I quite see that. We needn't say anything. But we can make him walk in front and from his gestures we also shall come to know which house it is.'

I think that subconsciously I had noticed the presence of the tall, thin, pimpish man for some seconds already as we stood there. He was the same tallish, sparish, small boned Sindi I had noted before on one of our several ups or downs of the street. It was almost as if his skin had a fruit-bloom of mauve on it, and it was obvious that he was straining to catch and understand our conversation – yet probable that he could not follow Pashto. I tried to warn Kaka sahib and whispered something, but he was not in a very reactive mood, having been upset by failure.

'I expect Muhammad Khan must know very well,' Kaka sahib was saying, 'because I think – I say I *think* – that Sikunder Khan has taken Muhammad Khan to that *chakla*-house on one occasion or two.'

At this point, even if the tallish, sparish Sindi who stood so near us had not spoken, I would have known from his eyes that he had confirmed what he had already suspected, for a look of the strangest

A Frieze of Dervishes

relief came into them. He took the step forward that brought him into bowing range, and he bowed – a very un-pimpish bow.

'You are Kaka sahib?' he asked deferentially, in Urdu.

Kaka sahib bowed – or in any case he inclined his head slightly – and said that he was.

'Forgive me if I speak wrong,' the man said, 'but I have watched you for some minutes, walking up, walking down, and it seems to me that you are searching for something – no, again, forgive me, for I know that you are a saint and not much interested in such things as' – (he coughed discreetly) – 'whores. Yet you are searching in this street, and I hear this gentleman your friend address you as Kaka sahib, and I hear you speak the name of Sikunder Khan and together with this the name of Muhammad Khan and it happens that I know a pair of Pathan gentlemen of these two names, and indeed one of them – Khan Sikunder Khan, your *murid*, if I mistake not – is lodging in my house at present and oh! ...' – his eyes slid up into his skull with the emotion of it – 'Oh, I would be so deeply obliged, *great* Kaka and Pir sain, if you would kindly take him away from my whorehouse instantly, for he is playing ravage with my ladies and with my business. I have begged of him to go, but he will not.'

'*Will* not ...?' Kaka sahib looked sideways at me again. I give him credit for behaving with great aplomb at this tricky moment. He had sweetened his voice, and yet allowed a hint of menace to show through it, as if perhaps he knew that the man was a snake and ready with all manner of knavery to trap the simple – or else it might be that it was Sikunder whom he knew to be the knave and not the whorehouse keeper. 'And *why* will he not?' he inquired in this new voice.

The man looked about him anxiously and when he finally spoke it was not to answer the question but to ask another one: 'If Sikunder Khan, your *murid*, should return to you of his own free will, would you beat him, oh Pir sahib?'

'Beat him!' Kaka sahib was so genuinely shocked that he was taken unawares. 'How can you ask such a wicked question!'

'Well, I thought that you might – never having had the honour of making your acquaintance: and Sikunder with whom I have spoken on the subject said that you *would*. Indeed it is for this reason that he is still with us, eating my food and sleeping without payment with my ladies, in any case with the two of them whose hearts are a-havoc of him.' He made as if to go down on one knee in the gutter but didn't quite. Instead he joined his hands together and held them up in supplication: 'Oh Kaka sahib, great Pir, can you *promise* that you will not beat him, no matter what?'

'And why must I make promises to you?' demanded Kaka sahib – but I think he was really rather pleased with the important impression that he was making, for by now a good many people had collected and they all seemed to know what it was about.

'Because, kind and honourable saint, if you cannot make favourable answers for me to carry back to Sikunder, I fear that he will not come out again to you – and, alas, that is bad for him, and for my ladies, and for my customers (who are much scared of the knife he carries) – moreover these two best ladies of mine threaten to leave me if I call the police. So you can see how bad it is for everyone, Pir sain – you too, yes? For now it is already more than a week that Sikunder is with us and' – his voice rose to a thin wail that twanged the hardest heartstring: 'I desire him to go!'

The other people who had gathered round were murmuring together now, siding with the whorehouse keeper and urging Kaka sahib, very respectfully, to give the promise that was asked of him. 'Be clement, O Kaka sahib,' they were murmuring: 'Show your bigness and your kindness.' But Kaka sahib still hesitated.

I pulled the whorehouse keeper aside: 'Tell me the truth. Does Sikunder really wish to return to Kaka sahib but fears to, because of punishments?'

'Oh yes, indeed he does, he fears heartily – but he longs to return for he has had enough of it and is tired, and just now he has seen Kaka sahib: he was standing on the balcony of my humble dwelling – yes, yes! *Look, Kaka sahib! Look!* Sikunder is now standing on the balcony of my humble dwelling, watching you and

A Frieze of Dervishes

beseeching you! He said it to me to say it to you – look! Just a few steps down the street: walk those few steps, Kaka sahib, please! See that humble dwelling with the balcony – there where is the picture of the gentleman tearing and rending at a lion and breaking its jaws with fisticuffs? That picture is for my Royal Fitness Pills, but – oh yes: see that lady with red and gold sari? Yes? See behind that lady; Sikunder, looking? Now you see? Look up and across, Kaka sahib!'

'Up and across!' cried the bystanders, their arms waving the 'up' and the 'across'.

We all looked up and across, at the poster of the man in combinations tearing and rending the lion by virtue of the Royal Fitness Pills, above it to the balcony, at a very large lady in red and gold with braided locks and jaws that seemed to be munching on nougat or else on something rubbery, and half hidden behind her, an unequivocally Pathan face, staring down on Kaka sahib in hope and apprehension.

Kaka sahib looked away at once and drew the skirt of his old military greatcoat across him with a gesture as noble as any that a king could make.

'You may tell Sikunder that there will be no punishments. I have said it.'

But the whorehouse keeper was unsatisfied: 'Finger-signal it, Kaka sahib. Finger-signal your message, so that he may believe.'

So Kaka sahib finger-signalled his message and there were whispers of approbation all about, and the Sindi whorehouse keeper now led us up into his humble dwelling by way of a narrow door and stairway, and called to Sikunder who came in silence towards Kaka sahib from a little room off the first floor landing and made a sort of bow before him, taking the sleeve of his garment and kissing it and saying: 'Forgive me for my wickednesses.'

There was a good deal of whispering and tittering going on, naturally, because this was a whorehouse during business hours. A number of narrow doors, concealing as many tiny paper-thin three-ply cubicles, stood open a crack down the passageway, the boarders being sincerely interested, and several of them being free

171

to take a peep. One who was not strictly speaking free was peeping nevertheless, shrouded in a sheet with a moustachy old gentleman trying to conceal himself behind, a feat perhaps impossible in so small a room. But Sikunder was unaware or in any case completely unselfconscious of the scene in which he was playing the lead.

Kaka sahib touched him on the head and said something about his wickednesses being forgiven but he must come home now, and Sikunder stood up from his bowing. He was indeed a large man, above six foot and solidly built. There was something dead-end kid about him – big, square, lusty but lost. He was not handsome but he had a certain air and his eyes were wonderfully innocent. It was easy to see why the whores should like him for a change from their usual seedy diet. He was dressed in an old pair of baggy, swashbuckling Pathan pantaloons and a sort of coat. He had many *tawiz* and talismans, including one tight round his neck on a cord. He had no socks, but he wore army boots, almost colourless, so long was it since they had smelt boot-polish, nor had they laces. His shirt, on the other hand, was rather fine: cerise and white-striped rayon with a floppy collar. I wondered if one of the ladies had given it to him. He shook hands with the whorehouse keeper and then laid his hand to his heart.

'*Salaam, Ustad*,' he said – which would mean 'Peace on you, Maestro', or something respectful of the kind.

Then he asked, and was granted, permission to take leave of the boarders and for a second I had a glimpse of a little thing like a debauched schoolgirl, pretty as a bird, but with tears in her eyes. She put a little narrow hand over her brow and lowered her head so that we should not see her sadness any more, and in the other hand held out a rose as big as a button. Sikunder took the rose gently and kissed it and put it behind his ear, and then, thinking better of it, put it instead inside his shirt, under his heart. For a moment he leaned down and rested his head against hers, sniffing the blue-shining blackness of her hair as if no one was there but her and him. The big lady with braided locks and the red and gold sari was weeping unrestrainedly but not jealously, and she managed a little wet smile when Sikunder said farewell to her, and as soon as it was

A Frieze of Dervishes

said she went off into an explosion of tears and had to run away as best she might, considering the narrowness of the passage and her own bulk, sobbing and banging first against one side partition and then against the other on this sorrowful dash to her room. I think we were all rather moved by the scene.

'Come,' said Kaka sahib.

The whorehouse keeper cleared his throat. 'Ahem, ahem. I was thinking that this Englishman gentleman would perhaps care to rest himself a little, after all that fatiguing walk.'

Kaka sahib had turned back to regard the man. 'No,' he said clearly.

'But it is quiet and clean, my house, as the gentleman can see – and my ladies quiet and clean ...'

'No,' said Kaka sahib, on the stairs with Sikunder behind him.

'No,' I said, partly in loyalty to Kaka sahib, and partly because I really did not want to stay.

'*Oooh!*' went the whorehouse keeper, a frantic little cry, because we were all three about halfway down the stairs to God's fresh air by now, slipping like pearls through his poor gesticulating fingers. 'But *Huzoors*! Turn back! Sikunder Khan sahib! Kaka sahib! Oh *you*! Turn back, noblemen, I pray you!' He looked beseechingly into our back-turned noble faces. 'Oh sirs, that Sikunder eats and takes his pleasure like tigers for a week or more, and where is my recompense? For I am naught but a poor whorehouse keeper!'

'And it is on account of your poverty and your calling, *Ustad*,' said Kaka sahib from the bottom of the staircase well, 'that I look for no alms or offerings.'

And with these dignified words ringing about the whorehouse stairs, we left.

* * *

By now the afternoon was drawing on, the siesta time was finished, and the street was already rather full. An hour or so later, as soon as the sun went down, the real busy time would start. Yet already the pavements were filling up nicely, and many more of the first-floor balconies contained their load of ladies, chewing betel-nut and waiting. Kaka sahib was in splendid fettle now. We were scarcely out of the whorehouse than he gathered us together on the pavement and started to explain what he had in mind – though he had had the delicacy to move a yard or two away from the door we had just left.

'We shall go home!' he was exclaiming. 'You too, Peter, for you are of us now and have been so helpful – thank you, my dear friend, for being so helpful during this bad time. We shall go home and we shall eat, and Sikunder shall cook it, and we shall rejoice that this matter is now behind us in the shadows of this dirty' – (spit) – 'place. In fact we shall not speak of it any more, and instead we shall eat chickens and perhaps also meat-bones – beef – filled with their marrow and cooked in *ghee*, and spinach served with them. And after these ... What after these? Sikunder? What else?'

'Pir sahib,' Sikunder said softly and without raising his eyes from the pavement where one of his big old army boots was wagging from side to side in embarrassment, pivoting on its heel: 'Pir sahib, my Kaka sahib, how can we have these things you speak of?' – and this brought Kaka sahib up with a little jolt, because of course none of these things that were being spoken of were possible without the money to buy them. The two others did not look at me at all, but if there were to be any question of a feast and of our eating it, it was clear that I must pay for it. Well? Why not? For some time past others had been paying for my feasting with great and ready generosity. It was right that it should be my turn now.

'Kaka sahib,' I said. '*I* will gladly provide the feast, if Sikunder will do the buying and the cooking of it.'

'*Psssst!*'

Kaka sahib and I both looked up in surprise. It had been a determined and at the same time an angry noise, probably uttered by a lady. It *was* a lady. We could see her now, by craning our necks a little: she was standing on her balcony, just above us. I moved out a step or two into the gutter in order to see her better, and I saw her upper lip curve and her lower lip wrinkle and the tip of a vermilion, *pān*-stained tongue peep out as she did it again:

A Frieze of Dervishes

'*Pssssst!* You talk of feasting?' she shouted down to us in fury. She was beautiful, in a bold very highly coloured way – like an oleograph of a gypsy, and a bit frightening.

'Yes,' said Kaka sahib coldly. 'But not with you, sister.'

'I?' She went off into a shriek of laughter. 'That's enough to curdle a girl's milk!' And all the people who happened to be passing and had stopped now to listen, looked at each other delightedly, and began giggling in sympathy. I realised only now that Sikunder had withdrawn himself as far as it was possible for him to do so, under the projection of the lady's balcony, up against the opening of a little *pān-sopāri* stall. But the lady was at it again:

'I? You suppose that I would feast from the same dish as *that* lout? I'd as soon fart in it.' She was leaning over the balustrade now and pointing under it towards where Sikunder stood pretending to be unaware of what was going on. 'That lout!' she repeated: 'That ... that ...' – and as she was for the moment too breathless with anger to frame another word, one of the bystanders stepped in and gave her one:

'That *bahin-chūt*?' he suggested.

'Yes! That *bahin-chūt*. Moreover I advise any and all of you gentlemen very strongly to have nothing to do with anyone he has had anything to do with during the last ...' (she counted on her fingers, rapidly) 'seven days, for not only he has got the Hot, but probably also all the other evils under moon and sun!'

'I have *not* got it!' announced Sikunder furiously as he came out of hiding and squared his chest at everybody.

'But of *course* he's got it!' shrieked the lady from above. 'You know where he's been ever since I kicked him out for not paying, the big ... the big ...' – but nobody helped her with names this time because everyone could see whom they were being aimed at, and Sikunder was certainly very large and capable of violence. 'He's been next door in that pest-house of the Hot and the Cold and all the other evils, and he hasn't emerged for a week!' Her voice had risen to a great shout as she threw her arm across to indicate her neighbours. '*And* he hasn't paid them either, so he's got it all free including the Hot – and now they dare to talk of feastings and rejoicements!'

'Silence!' shouted Kaka sahib, and such was his authority that Sikunder went limp and the people stood back a little, and up above a man came out onto the balcony and pulled the lady indoors after him and we could hear a great smack and a squawk through the shutters that he had banged together behind them.

'I know what to do with you,' Kaka sahib said to Sikunder. 'Come.'

* * *

'I am not a hard man nor a tyrant,' Kaka sahib was saying to me, as if Sikunder did not exist or in any case could not hear – and I dare say he could not hear, because he was a couple of paces behind us. 'And I understand everything.'

We were marching at immense speed, the pace set by Kaka sahib. Already we had marched through the market square, where we had found Muhammad and with him, waiting patiently, a tough but somewhat scruffy-looking Pathan (only one) and we had gathered them to us – and I suppose that Sikunder explained to them, for Kaka sahib did not – and we continued the march. Up the cliff-face road, past Masum's Tower we went, along the ridge, marching, beneath the garden of the great clocktower dedicated to the Literacy Campaign, in the lee of the rising ground that supports the Collector's secretariat, past peepul trees and gardens – rolling up again the path that I had so carelessly unrolled that morning in the sunshine. The sun still shone, and huge clouds, cumulonimbus, back-lit, towering, Tiepolo, filled the sky. Kaka sahib continued:

'I was for those years in the Police Department and not always the qalandar you see, and I know very well what men like to do – eating and sleeping and drinking and whoring, and there is no harm in it and much delight – except that, yes, you have to decide about these things. If you like that business *very* much – as Sikunder likes it and is forever at it – it is of no use to sit under a tree in the spare

A Frieze of Dervishes

time and hope that peace will come into your heart, for it is only a fatigued little peace that then can come, not the true peace, and more often a sadness.' He stopped, to look at me. 'True?'

'True, true,' I admitted. 'But I thought that when a man, like Sikunder for example, attached himself to a *murshid* for spiritual guidance and in order to start out upon the Way, he would forswear all such whoring and would allow himself to be ruled entirely by the orders of his *murshid*.'

I had not got beyond halfway in this sentence before Kaka sahib started waving his hands to stop me. 'No, no! You have not understood. That would be a different matter, and of course if Sikunder were truly on the Way, what you said would be so. But Sikunder is not on the Way. He calls me Pir sahib, I know, and I am a Pir, but I am not his *murshid*: and I am not anyone's *murshid*, anyone's guide, nor have ever I had a *murshid* to guide me – for although in the beginning time I have tried to understand the talk they use and those *dhikrs* they recite and their drums and their chantings and the secret words of God, and although all these things are good for some, they only made me upset and I came no nearer to the illumination. Each man must find his way, and I have searched in my way without words or recitations and alas I have not yet quite found. How then could I be the *murshid* of anyone, for what could I teach – except that God is *there* ...' – he pointed to the heavens – 'and that He is also everywhere else, and that we are *here*.' He stopped and when next he spoke his voice had shrunk away to a little pinpoint of sound: '*But who are we* ...?'

'Yes, even that ... Who are *we*?'

After a moment he said: 'I have started on the Way and must continue upon it and if you will think in your head you will see at once that someone like me, or anyone, must have food to put into his stomach or he will die before he has come to the end of the Way, and it is my great desire to reach the end before I die.' There was a wandering look on his face, but our arrival at the foot of the ramp leading up the embankment to the railway line and the suspension bridge that towered above us now, broke in on what he was saying.

'The bridge,' I said, without really thinking of bridges. 'But where are we going so fast?'

'To the shrine of Hazrat Fulano Shah,' he whispered, 'but *sh-h*. I don't want Sikunder to hear.'

'Fulano Shah?' I whispered back. 'It's not to your *durgah* then? Which is your shrine?'

'I have none.'

'But you are *gadi-nisshin*. Muhammad told me.'

'Oh dear,' he said falteringly: 'Yes, he did say it. He does sometimes – and so does Sikunder. They think it makes it easier to get alms and offerings for me if they tell people I am *gadi-nisshin*. It is very wrong of them, but of course it *does* sometimes make it easier. Yet there is no harm, either in Sikunder or in Muhammad, no evil. Muhammad is a little soft, and Sikunder is a little headstrong, but their hearts are true and they beg alms for me and bring me whatever is given in God's name.' He looked back over his shoulder at his two men and then said: 'And as a matter of fact it would perhaps be impossible for either of them to find work because neither of them at all cares for working. I think that is why they are content to remain with me, though it is a hard life for them sometimes.'

Down below us, in a curve of the riverbank, lay Khwajo Khizr's little island and his shrine. Dark trees encircled it. Kaka sahib bowed to it. We walked over the suspension bridge. Rohri, on the farther bank, looked older than ever and more ramshackle in the evening light. The sun as it sank westwards had grown more yellow and the sky more pink.

'Kaka sahib, Kaka sahib,' Sikunder was saying earnestly from a pace behind us. 'Listen to me. I have *not got* the *Hot!*'

* * *

Somewhere hidden in the very stomach of Rohri town, with the little lanes winding themselves like guts all round about, is the shrine of Hazrat Fulano Shah. I had never before seen it nor heard of it. It has a rope of bells slung across the entrance, as with many

A Frieze of Dervishes

shrines. The wooden clappers hang well clear of the bell mouth so that a grateful pilgrim can reach up and clang at one of them as he leaves. Unlike the majority of shrines, the entrance to this one was closed and locked.

Kaka sahib led his party up to the gate and banged upon it, calling out for the dervish who would presumably be there to act as guardian, and in a moment a little person did peep out timidly from the shadows, peering through the bars at us. Perhaps as a group we may have seemed a little intimidating – with Kaka sahib so large and bearded, Sikunder so bandit-looking, and the hired bandit so bandit too, and only Muhammad and myself of fairly ordinary appearance to offset all this solid, hostile-looking bulk.

'Yes?' inquired the little person through the bars. 'You want something, gentlemen?'

'Open,' said Kaka sahib, quite nicely, but firmly.

The setting sun struck orange on the backs of bells and through the little person's wispy hair as he pretended to fumble with the lock. But he didn't open the gate.

'Call the *gadi-nisshin*, then,' I said to him.

'Oh but sirs, Pir sain is at his house and is not in the *durgah-sharif* at present – but if you permit I will run to tell him that you are here ...'

'... to tell him that he must come,' corrected Kaka sahib. 'At once.'

'Yes, yes, of course, sir ...'

A second or two later a door in the wall, ten feet away from us, flicked open and then closed behind a little figure that had flown out like a paper dart and was gone whisking away into the silence.

We waited.

'I remember only that he is fat,' announced Kaka sahib, busy with his thoughts.

'Who?'

'The *gadi-nisshin* of this shrine.'

Sikunder pulled at my elbow. 'Why have we come here?' he whispered in an odd voice. 'Do you know? Did Kaka sahib tell you? What is this place?'

'I don't know,' I whispered back. 'Don't *you* know them?'

Kaka sahib had caught the sound of whispers and turned to us: 'What are you saying?'

'Nothing. I was just asking Sikunder why we have come here,' I said.

Kaka sahib glanced quickly at Sikunder.

'Is it because of me?' Sikunder asked suspiciously.

'Well … It is because of …' – but Kaka sahib did not have to finish his sentence – and seemed relieved not to have had to finish it – for now the *gadi-nisshin* was arriving, an immense old gentleman swathed in a cashmere shawl against the chill of night. He was courtly and charming and rather flustered from having come so fast to receive us. He had to sit down for a little in order to regain his composure. Sikunder was getting more and more suspicious. We were all inside the forecourt of the shrine now, and soon the *gadi-nisshin* was in condition to give ear to Kaka sahib who was murmuring softly into it. The *gadi-nisshin* nodded with wisdom and sympathy. Sikunder plucked at my arm again.

'They are up to some bad, those two,' he hissed at me.

'No, no, Sikunder,' I said, to comfort him. 'It can be nothing bad.'

But nevertheless I wondered what it was and much wished to know.

'Hm, hm, hm, hm,' went the *gadi-nisshin* on a rising arpeggio, nodding his head so that his chins telescoped in and out of each other. 'I see, I see.' He turned to call his dervish. 'Light the lanterns.'

So the lanterns were lit.

The tomb was in an open court at a level slightly below where we stood, and the court itself was surrounded by a balustrade through the openings of which tendrils of greenery came groping. There was a domed building, perhaps another tomb, alongside, but it was all on a very modest scale, and high around us on three sides reared the rickety homes of Rohri citizens. Kaka sahib had accompanied the *gadi-nisshin* down the few steps that led to the open court, and he now beckoned to Sikunder to join him. Sikunder caught my arm, urging me to come too, but I slipped free and he had to go alone.

A Frieze of Dervishes

I did not hear what Kaka sahib said, but I saw Sikunder's face close instantly. Then Kaka sahib seemed to be cajoling him, but the face remained closed and expressionless – not even scowling. The *gadi-nisshin* came wheezing and waddling across and said something to Sikunder, laying his hand on the younger man's arm. Sikunder stood there, shuddering but silent. I went down the steps and joined the group.

The *gadi-nisshin* smiled in a sort of way, rather anxiously, and moved to one side of the court, calling out to his dervish: 'Allahdino!' – and the little person darted up, his hands together over his heart. He nodded as he received his orders.

'I am telling Allahdino to extinguish that big lantern over the tomb,' the *gadi-nisshin* explained to Kaka sahib. 'Perhaps your man is shy. But modesty is good. There is too much light, perhaps. There! That's better.'

The big light over the tomb had been extinguished and now the old gentleman turned to me with a gesture that seemed also to include Muhammad and the new bandit who had followed us down into the court – a gesture of ushering us all up the steps again to the forecourt. 'Come, the rest of you,' he said: 'No, no. Not you, Sikunder, please. Kaka sahib, kindly tell your man to remain below …'

Muhammad nudged me as we went up the steps: 'This man that I have brought wishes to know exactly how much you are going to pay him.'

I looked at the bandit and said: 'Kaka sahib will decide.'

'All right,' the bandit said: 'But I want Kaka sahib to decide now.'

'You can see that "now" is a bad moment. Be patient.'

'I have been patient for hours.'

'Then be patient for a few more minutes …'

But suddenly a shout from the court below brought us wheeling round in our tracks:

'I will not!'

It was Sikunder. He was backing his way up the steps like a swordsman on the defensive. Beyond him, and below, stood Kaka

181

sahib, his face grey with anger and his fists opening and closing themselves, while the poor distracted old *gadi-nisshin* wrung his hands as if he was unable to grasp at all what the matter might be.

'But what is this?' cried the old gentleman in his bewilderment. 'It is all so simple, so *simple*. Sikunder, you have but to ...'

'But I have not got the hot!' shouted Sikunder in a paroxysm of anger. 'I tell you I have not got the hot!' – and with this he turned and grabbed my sleeve, trying to drag me with him out of the place, but the bandit snatched at my other arm to hold me, and Kaka sahib shouted from below: 'Hold him!' – and although it was clear that he meant Sikunder, it was I who became held, and Sikunder had gone.

'Fools!' shouted Kaka sahib. 'Fools! Go after him!'

I had had enough. I wrenched myself free of the bandit and made for the gates, but he followed close behind and grabbed me by the shoulder, shouting 'It's all right, it's all right, it's only my money I want – and the others haven't got any' – so running along together in this ludicrous manner I pulled some money out of my pocket and passed it to him. He stopped running at once. 'Thank you!' he called after me.

Sikunder had of course already disappeared round the corner.

* * *

I stopped running too when I had rounded the corner, feeling very stupid. What was I running for – except, perhaps, in sympathy with Sikunder. All my sympathy was with Sikunder in this affair. Kaka sahib had behaved badly. I walked on down the little dark alley, thinking back on the day that was now dying and as I rounded another corner a voice went '*shh!*' from just above my head. I looked up and saw Sikunder's face peering over a wall.

'Sikunder!'

'*Shh!* But listen!'

The sound of voices wrangling in the distance came to us – Kaka sahib for one, and the slightly petulant voice would be the old gentleman.

A Frieze of Dervishes

'That old man!' exclaimed Sikunder, coming out from behind the wall. 'Do you know, Peter? He wished me to squat behind the tomb and untie my cord and lean forward in some manner and then to touch the tomb in some manner and then say some words and then drink something after, so as to be cured of the Hot – I, who have not got it!' He stopped and made a gesture of finality. 'I am never going back.'

'What do you mean?'

'I am never going back to Kaka sahib. He is becoming worse each day, more and more police.'

'But if you do not go back, what will you do?'

'I will find some other qalandar. There are many, many ...'

'Yes, there are many: but I think you will not easily find a qalandar as good as Kaka sahib – even if he is sometimes rather police. And if you cannot find one, what will you do?'

'I do not know ...' He paused. 'Yes, but I *do* know. I have a place to go ... Peter, will you like to come too? It is a place where no one will pull you or push you in this manner, and no one will ask anything of you that you do not wish to do, and where everyone is happy.'

'And where is this paradise place?'

'Peter sahib, Peter, have you three rupees left – or have you, better, *six* rupees? Because to buy half a *seer* is double the goodness of a quarter *seer*, and we should not arrive with empty hands.'

'And what is it that we shall buy half a *seer* of, then?'

'You will see. It is to be a surprise for you: you should not ask about it till you are shown. You understand? A half *seer*, good: we shall also buy a little sugar and almond nuts. Come. Silently.'

I hesitated. What about poor Kaka sahib?

Behind us the distant voices still wrangled, though half-heartedly now, it seemed, and the first shrill noisiness had gone.

'Come!' Sikunder said, pulling at my coat.

7
The World is a...

'SIT HERE PLEASE,' SIKUNDER SAID, pushing me down onto a little seat with heavy twisted-wire legs, 'and stay here till I come back to get you. I will not be very long. And don't look out of the door, in case Kaka sahib comes in search of me or of you. Do you understand?' He looked earnestly into my face to see if I had really understood. I was able to convince him, apparently, so he left me.

I had been put to sit in a minute coffee house in a side lane. Sikunder knew the proprietor and had arranged it with him. Sukkur, on the other bank of the Indus, is a biggish town and well accustomed to visitors: Rohri is a little enclosed town and the people in the coffee house fell silent when I sat down amongst them. I kept my eyes on the doorway, but I could feel theirs on me, watching. After a while their chatter began again, tentatively, like putting a foot into the water to test it before plunging. I believe they would have liked to question me, but for my part I preferred not to talk for the present. I thought of Kaka sahib, and wondered if I had behaved ill in leaving with Sikunder in this fashion. Then I thought of the day as a whole again and then I stopped thinking, placidly content to let the waves of whatever was afoot close over my head. There was nothing to be gained by trying to make sense of other people's lives – Kaka sahib's, Sikunder's. But quite soon Sikunder was back again, carrying a bundle in a bulging whitish cloth. He was accompanied by a Sindi with black salwars and a green shirt.

'He is my friend,' Sikunder explained to me. 'He has a tonga-cart. And he says that since *we* have *this*' – he patted his bundle – '*he*

Saints of Sind

will be happy to drive us to the place and stay there with us, because it is a little far for feet, you see.'

I shook hands with the tonga-man and said that we were much obliged to him and he said that he was much obliged to us, and in due course we went to where his tonga stood waiting. He lit a big lantern and slung it under the axle, then clambered up to his box. I clambered up beside him, in front, because I like to see where I am going. Sikunder sat behind, back-to-back with us. The pony was grey and as big as a camel.

The driver, or else the pony, must have known the way blindfold, and certainly we could not otherwise have found it. From the point where we left the metalled road there was no more than a track, recognisable as such to begin with by the fact of cactus hedges to either side of it. But later the cactus hedges seemed to have dissolved into thin air and the rough jungle country to left and right of us could just as easily have been the track. Night had fallen by now, of course. Behind us the lights of Rohri winked and blinked and stars were out in the skies. The moon would be coming up very soon. The lantern swinging underneath from the axle threw tormented, broken images of wheels to left and right, and of four legs bodiless in front of us.

I think we must have travelled three miles, four perhaps, before we reached the first grove of trees, though it was difficult to estimate distance in terms of time and the tonga's speed. We would go forward at a brisk trot for some tens of yards, flop suddenly into a pothole, creak, shiver and remain miraculously unspilled, and there would then follow a long, painful passage during which the wheels scarcely seemed to turn at all. The moon was just coming over the horizon, enormously swollen at this first moment of her appearance, and the second grove of trees became visible. I could see the shape the grove made against the night-sky – an up-turned saucer, and posed in the centre of it an upturned teacup: and now that we were drawing nearer I thought I could even identify the trees. The saucer would be a circle of tangled mimosa, and the cup that rose in the centre of it would be a grove of neem trees. The neems were larger and more splendid than anything in the visible vicinity.

The World is a...

'This is the place,' Sikunder said, as the driver reined in his pony. Then he jumped down and went up to the mimosas. There was no sign of any habitation.

'Peace be upon you!' Sikunder shouted into the mimosas at the top of his voice. 'It is I, Sikunder the Pathan!'

There was complete silence, so he shouted again.

A light suddenly showed itself through the mimosas and then was lost, as if there might be just this one point where the hedge was thinner than elsewhere. When next I saw the light it was much closer, and in a moment it appeared framed in foliage, and held high by the man carrying it. There was a gate of some kind, and the man's shadowed face was visible behind the lantern, trying to make certain of his visitors.

'Ah, it *is* Sikunder. Come in. Peace be upon you. And upon you, too, oh Tongawala, my friend.' He opened the gate. 'And this is ... who?'

'It is the English Peter – and see what we have brought you!'

Sikunder now raised his bundle with a flourish and carried it up to the man's nose so that he could sniff it. 'Half a *seer*! Also almond nuts.'

'Half a *seer*?' The man looked closely at me. Then he smiled. 'Peace be upon you.' He had a ploughed and ravaged face, heavy lines dragging it down from nose to jaw, and eyebrows that joined across his forehead like a longbow. He smelt of attar of Henna. We went in through the opening and under the light of his lantern the gate turned into an old crate lid.

Now that we were inside I could see that the mimosas had been cut and trained back in such a manner that they formed a sort of protective zareba all round a clearing. It would be possible, no doubt, to brave the mimosa thorns and squeeze through at several points, but at one only, apparently, had a formal opening been left, and it was this that was closed by the crate lid. The clearing was not very large – small enough, in any case, to be adequately lit by three big lanterns, one carried by the man who had received us, the second set on the ground ahead of us, and the third hanging outside a crumbling little cottage in one corner. It hung above a square of mosaic pavement, and to the left of the pavement was a daïs raised a couple of feet higher than the general level of the ground. The daïs was patterned in mosaic too, both top and sides. A small mimosa had been made to spread itself like an umbrella over it, and a couple of men were sitting under this mimosa umbrella while others squatted on the pavement, occupied with something that I could not see till they edged round on their hunkers to look at us as we came near. Then I saw that it was a fighting cock that they were busy with, examining its neck. One of the men in this group gathered up the fighting cock and came forward to greet us. The bird was in the crook of his arm now, with its long spurred legs hanging down beneath it. Its head made nervous, twitching movements and its bead eyes flicked. The man stroked it with love. It had a wound on its neck. Another man had come up to me too, a small person with a white beard and wrinkles and a very peculiar appearance. All these things I was aware of simultaneously and in a somewhat confused fashion.

'I've seen you in church,' the strange person said at once, in English.

I stood there in astonishment. In church? In English?

'Yes, yes, in church, it was,' he continued, smiling in quite a composed way.

But never before, in church or out of it, had I seen this little man, nor anyone like him. He was very small: not above five foot, I judged: he had white curly hair, a dark, squeezed-up, wrinkled, white-bearded baby's face, a long grey shift to his shins, and what looked like a loongi peeping out under it. His ankles were laden with copper rings and his neck with necklaces and talismans. But it was his expression that was so peculiar – a pixie agelessness.

'They call me Jackie. And you see for many years I was living at No. 44, Plaistow Lane, London, EC8.'

So that explained the fluent English.

'Oh, I see,' I said, as if it also explained everything else.

'Master Jackie,' said the man with the fighting cock. 'Master Jackie.'

'Yes,' said Master Jackie. 'And now I will introduce you to the other gentlemen.'

We turned to the others, to the man with the fighting cock, the man with a broken ravaged face who had received us at the crate lid, a man with a long pink shirt and a moustache of blue-black silko, and others in this frieze – and all of them with an indefinable air of disintegration, all except Sikunder Khan.

Sikunder was busy giving instructions to a thin, grubby-looking creature with fingers like chestnut twigs. I watched the fingers untie the bundle we had brought and open it out on the ground. Thin leaves, green – the thin man leaned down and smelt them, his nose twitching and snuffling. So that's what it was – Indian hemp, hashish.

'Master Jackie, Master Jackie,' called the thin man. 'The pots now, please.'

The man with the fighting cock was talking: 'He's got a hurt. Here on his neck, you see.' He folded the feathers back on the bird's neck.

'Fighting?' I asked, examining the wound dutifully.

'Yes. Fighting. He's old now.'

'Perhaps he's really too old to fight any more.'

'I expect so – but he enjoys it so much. Was it you that brought the bundle?' he asked, nodding towards it.

'*Bhang*,' I said. 'Yes.'

'Good. Good. It will take a little while. Come with me and say "peace on you" to father.'

So he took me into the cottage in the corner of the clearing. An immovable old man in rags was on the ground beside a fire.

'Father!' shouted my companion at the top of his voice. 'Here is a *ferangi* to see you. (What is your name? Peter? You are English?) It is English Peter – and he has come with Sikunder Khan.'

'Eh?'

'He's not really our father, or anybody's father,' the man said confidentially, 'but he minds the teapot – *don't you, father? I'm telling Peter sahib that you mind the teapot*.' He reduced his voice to talking strength once more: 'He's always been here as long as anyone can remember. And the other two who live here are Master Jackie and Turabaz. You haven't seen Turabaz? The one with the earring? You will in a minute. Perhaps he's busy. Where's Turabaz?' he called out to someone through the door and received a reply I did not catch. 'Yes, he's busy, but he won't be long, I expect. You've struck a lucky night. You can enjoy, too. He and Jackie and father, they're always here. And Samuel as a rule. It's Samuel preparing the *bhang*, that very thin one. Then the rest of us come when we want to, or when any of us has the money, you see.'

'I see. What is this place, then? Not a shrine of some kind, is it?'

'Well, I don't know. Someone once said that that was a shrine – that thing in the corner: it looks a bit like one, doesn't it, but I don't know who can be inside it. *Do you know who's in there, father?*' he shouted through cupped hands.

'Yes,' the old thing replied, nodding and mumbling. He had no teeth so that his mouth shut itself much more closed than it otherwise would, and this caused his beard to stick straight out in front of him. 'Yes,' he said. His face was thin, but his body was padded into a pyramid of rags.

'He's difficult to talk to,' the other man said. 'Let's go outside.'

We stood for a minute or two in the doorway, looking out into the clearing and talking quietly. Moonlight filtered through the branches of the trees above us, dusty blue and beautiful, and there was a pool of yellow light under the trees as smooth as amber. It was peaceful and withdrawn.

The thin man they said was Samuel was on his hunkers before a big wide bowl in which he was washing the hashish leaves. He poured out the water of one washing as we stood and watched him, and refilled the bowl. He would be a Christian, presumably: probably a casteless Hindu convert. Master Jackie was presumably a Christian as well.

'How many washings?' I asked, nodding towards the hemp leaves.

'Three.'

Master Jackie had squatted down with a pestle and mortar ready while Samuel rinsed the sodden leaves in his fingers. I heard a little growl at our feet and, looking down, saw a minute dog, though not a puppy, lying curled up immediately in our path.

'Out of the way, there!' my companion said to it. 'Get along now, lazy,' and the little dog snarled. 'They don't do a stroke of work, you know,' he complained.

'What could it do, for example?'

'It could watch, couldn't it? They're always sleeping.'

He pushed the little dog out of the way with the side of his foot and we walked on, leaving it snarling furiously. I saw Master Jackie stiffen and swing round.

'Cutlet! What's Cutlet crying about?' he asked me fiercely in English as I reached his side.

'Cutlet! That little dog, do you mean?'

'Yes. He's mine. Did you kick him?'

'Certainly not!'

'Did that big beast kick him, then? I bet he did.'

'No, he didn't.'

'Then why is poor Cutlet crying so? Cutlet, Cutlet! Come here to daddy!' he called and the little dog came to him to be looked over for broken bones. 'These orientals,' Master Jackie muttered: 'Did they kick him then, the brutes? In London they'd lock that beast up in no time, they would. Dogs always know who's good and who's bad. They lick the good and bite the bad, don't they, my Cutlet?'

'Jackie!' Samuel was trying to attract his attention back to the work. 'Give me that pestle.'

'Here's Turabaz,' said the man with the fighting cock as someone came out of the mimosas: an oval face, clean-shaven, a shock of black hair and an earring in the right ear. We were introduced.

'Welcome,' Turabaz said.

'Thank you.'

'You like *bhang*, then?'

'I've never had it,' I admitted. 'I've had hashish in other forms – *Kif*, *Madjoun* – but never *bhang* before.'

'Oh, you will like it, I am sure.'

'Yes, I am sure I shall like it.'

The washings were complete now, and Master Jackie was industriously pounding the leaves in his mortar so that the clearing rang to the sound of brass – *clang-clang-calang*. 'It won't be long,' he shouted to me above the noise he was making. Had he decided after all not to pretend that we had kicked Cutlet, then? 'Have you got a hanky?' he called out.

I temporised: 'What for?'

'Not for blowing. For straining the *bhang*.'

'I'm sorry,' I said, 'but as a matter of fact I haven't,' though as a matter of fact I had.

'Never mind. This will do' – and he produced a terrible-looking old rag from his pocket.

'Wait,' I said quickly, fumbling in my pocket. 'After all, I believe …. Yes, after all, as a matter of fact I *have*' – and I handed over my clean handkerchief.

Jackie took a big brass pot and laid my handkerchief across its mouth and then poked a depression into the cloth and filled the depression with as much of the pounded hemp leaf as it would hold. I turned to say something to Sikunder who had been standing near a moment ago, but he had disappeared.

'Where's Sikunder?'

'Oh …?' Samuel looked round and about. 'I don't know. I expect he must be busy, then. But he won't be long.' He was pouring milk, or possibly a mixture of water and milk, over the leaves. Jackie was holding the handkerchief firm. Slowly the liquid dripped through the cloth into the pot. Samuel helped it a bit every now and again, scrabbling with his twig-thin fingers in the green, green fluid. I turned my face away – though I cannot be sure why this scrabbling should distress me when the earlier process of rinsing the leaves had not. I took comfort from the thought that cooking would sterilise everything anyway. Master Jackie was busy pounding almonds in his mortar now, and when he had finished he poured them into a second brass pot that was waiting there. He added sugar.

'There!' announced Samuel, transferring the handkerchief with its squelching spinach-like contents to the mouth of the second pot. Then he poked his finger in to make the depression deeper and added more of the rest of the washed and pounded leaves, for which there had been no room earlier, added a little more milk too, and a little more water.

Four times they strained it, or maybe five, backwards and forwards from the first to the second pot, sipping at it from time to time and making bird noises with their lips in an attempt to taste more truly, these extraordinary men, sipping, eyes to the moon, sipping, tasting.

Samuel added a sprinkling of a spice I could not identify, and a little more sugar.

'Not too much sugar!' warned Turabaz – and then turned to me. 'But the taste would be bad without any. Sniff it. Samuel! Give it to the *ferangi* to sniff.'

I sniffed it.

'Sikunder!' shouted Turabaz. 'Hurry up! It's ready – nearly ready now. Come everybody,' he went on, shepherding us towards the mosaic pavement outside the cottage door.

We arranged ourselves in a rough circle.

'You don't cook it, then?' I asked.

'No. Why cook it?'

'I don't know. I suppose I thought ...'

'Only grass,' explained Master Jackie as he handed over the pot to Turabaz. 'Mild as mild. Mild as beer.'

'First for English Peter,' Turabaz said, handing me the pot: 'because he was the giver of it.'

'No. *Last* for me,' I said, 'because I was the giver of it.'

'All right,' Jackie said: 'Then first my Lord and Father,' and he pointed at Turabaz. 'He's not my real father – but he's my *true* father, and he feeds me. Don't you, father?' He gave a rapid translation in Sindi. Then he said to me: 'I am living here for ever, now. No more troubles for Master Jackie.'

Turabaz had his face in the pot and I don't know what he was thinking. The others waited in an eager silence.

The pot went round and everyone drank from it in turn. Soon it would be me. I looked at the circle of lost faces, eighteenth-century back-street debauchees, dismaying – and then Sikunder came up from behind us and leaned over into the circle, saying:

'Turabaz says now you, Peter – before all those others.'

'No. I'm last. It's all arranged.'

'All right, then. You mean you want the *bhang* first?'

'No. *Last*,' I repeated.

'Oh well, do what you want.'

'In that case,' the tonga-man said, getting up from beside me on the pavement, 'I think I'll ... out of the way, there, little dog!'

'Cutlet, Cutlet!' I called to it, snapping my fingers. It certainly was a very stupid little dog: always under people's feet. Sikunder picked it up and it didn't bite him. He sat down in the place left empty by the tonga-man, the dog in his arms, but the dog jumped out.

'Cutlet!' I called, and it came and sniffed at me.

'That's not Cutlet!' Master Jackie shouted from the other side of the circle. 'Do you think Cutlet would speak to you again after the last time? *That* innocent little dog is one of Cutlet's brethren.'

'Oh, I see. What his name?'

'He hasn't got a name.' He paused. 'You know, I have searched and searched for a good English name but I cannot find one.'

'Rover?' I suggested.

The brass pot had reached Sikunder's neighbour now and I saw the man drink from it. Then he handed it to Sikunder and Sikunder raised it to drink from it in his turn.

'Rover!' Master Jackie was exclaiming scornfully. 'But what I want is a fine name – *like* Cutlet, but *not* Cutlet.'

'Hamlet, possibly?'

'Hamlet, Hamlet...? Is that an English name?'

'No, perhaps not, quite. Hamlet was Prince of Denmark.'

'Now you, Peter,' Sikunder said, handing me the pot.

'Prince of...?'

'Denmark.'

I put the pot to my lips – the taste of brass on teeth, the liquid on the tongue. I took a deep draught. It was light and not disagreeable, thin, faintly aromatic, very green.

The World is a...

* * *

A quarter of an hour had passed, rather more, twenty minutes or twenty-five, even. It would be quite soon now. We sat on patiently, talking a little and waiting for it to begin, a circle of men under trees, lit by the moon and three lanterns – the pink shirt, Turabaz and his earring, Samuel with his chestnut twigs, the green shirt of the tonga-man ... No, not the tonga-man: he had left us some time before. Others were there, then: Master Jackie and the man with the ravaged face and the man with the fighting cock whose name I could not ...

'... quite remember, Sikunder, please, his name?'

'Oh *he*...?'

'Yes. The green shirt also of the tonga-man, your friend.'

'Yes. He, too.'

'Exactly! Later I'll ask their names.'

'Yes. Later, perhaps – if God wills.'

Something was stirring already, I dare say, and Sikunder's voice had seemed a little odd: very clear, with neat edges, but the cadences peculiar. Mine too? I said something in order to listen to it. Everything was very clear and neatly edged, as a matter of fact – voices, colours. Sikunder was laughing softly to himself and the pot was coming round again, just in case. We all looked pleased.

This was as it should be. It is most important to be good-tempered and without worries when you enter the Gates of *Bhang*. It is true of all the hashish derivatives as everyone who has ever taken hashish knows, and there is always Baudelaire to warn those who approach the gates for the first time ... '... I presume you have taken the precaution of choosing well your moment for this adventurous expedition ...' Perfect leisure. No duties awaiting your return and demanding punctuality or precision. No troubles in the home, no lovesickness. Baudelaire will tell you that in hashish the least unease may prove an anguish, the least of chagrins torture.

I searched my heart for anguish and my conscience for my duty. None. Then I looked slowly round the circle – for to be in sympathy with your companions is important too – I looked slowly round, searching their eyes for sympathy, and finding it each moment deeper and more exuberant, because everything in *bhang* is more exuberant: friendship more keen and love more rich and hate more bitter – the sun more bright the moon more mad and also fun more funny. I had begun to laugh, moreover. I am not sure why. Perhaps because Sikunder was laughing.

We were all helpless with laughter soon, laughter that had spread like the blue flame round a well-trimmed wick, round the circle of us – and then there stepped into our midst, over our backs, the tonga-man in his green shirt, but much preoccupied with a watch that he had taken unlaughingly from his pocket and had placed against his ear. He brought it down from his ear and gave it a terrible shaking.

'That's better,' he said. 'It's going again now.'

He held it up on its chain for all to see, and it hung there, turning in the night, a turnip, a heavenly body of a watch, a silver moon.

'Can you all hear it now?' he asked us, proud to possess so fine an object.

'Yes, yes, we can hear it, we can hear it.'

Hear it? There was scarcely room for it in all this grove of trees. I could hear nothing else but the turnip's heart a-beating, the brilliant, shining heartbeats. It interfered with my laughing. And then great greyish shivers took me, driving up from the depths of me with the frantic urgency of people trying to escape, and I don't know how long I remained in this condition while life went ticking out of the silver turnip. I knew only that my eyes had become very large and my face smaller, and that my feet grew cold. Also my hands. It was the coldness not of winter but of dying – perhaps of having died. It scared me horribly. I tried to get up onto my butter legs but they declined and I sat down again – remembering nevertheless to fold my legs safely under me, not from good manners this time, as in mosques or even private houses, but because I had read of what happened to Sir Richard Burton in *bhang*, how one of his legs had revolved upon its knee as axis, and how he both felt and heard it strike against and pass through his shoulder at each revolution. I wished to avoid this experience. But after a while the fear left me and I set my legs free once more, to test them. I crept secretly away from the circle, surprised that I had ever been afraid, and it seemed to be hours later that I reached the little daïs of a raft in those far, far, far mosaic seas and established myself upon it. I decided to take my shoes off, for comfort. Later still a voice with the qualities of chocolate said in my car:

'You're next, but hurry.'

Looking, I saw a crocheted vest with a body showing through it in little stars of flesh, chocolate flesh, and an arm sticking out of an armhole with an incandescent shirt hung limp across it – pink.

'Put on your shoes and hurry,' said the voice of chocolate.

'I am unable to hurry.'

I was looking at the pink, moreover.

'I am *helping* you to hurry.' And at this he reached down into the mosaic for my shoes, turned one upside-down and banged it on the daïs – to shake out the scorpions. But, despite my preoccupation with pink, it was evident to me that instead of scorpions a procession of little dogs would come tottering out if he banged it once again – Cutlet and Hamlet. Who else? Goblet, maybe? I took the second of my shoes and banged it on the daïs, conjuring its inmates out of the toe: 'Tablet! Piglet! Gullet! Giblet!' Why should it ever end? I sat there, waiting for it to begin: 'Gimlet! Mullet! Skillet! ...' And raising my voice to a shout: 'Master Jackie, Master Jackie! Who is next?' – and his answer sailed back to me: 'You're next, but hurry, hurry! She's getting fretful.'

'Yes, hurry,' the deep chocolate voice said: 'She's *got* fretful already.'

'Who?'

'The lady.'

I put down my emptied shoes.

'So there's a lady, then?'

'Of course. Over there, in the mimosas. You're the last, so hurry.'

'But ...' I was looking round at my companions.

'You said you wanted to be last.'

'Yes, but that was for the *Bhang* ...' and he cut in, shrugging his chocolate shoulders:

'Never mind, if you don't want. Here!' He suddenly threw down the pink shirt onto the daïs. 'Don't let any of them get this. I'm going back.' And he went back into the mimosas.

I sat looking at the pink shirt, each moment more aware of its pinkness. Then I stood up and looked at it, and after a moment I found that the man with the ravaged face was standing beside me looking at it too. He put out his hand to it, and I said 'Don't touch!' and he looked oddly at me.

'It's not yours,' he said.

'And it's not yours either.'

I hesitated, trying to determine exactly what it could be – because already it was clear that it was much more than it seemed.

Master Jackie had joined us and was whispering in my ear.

'Shall we hang it in the tree?'

'Why?'

'It will be beautiful.'

'All right.'

We hung it in the tree, carefully, spreading its arms and its tails so that it became like a canopy. Then we sat regarding it.

'I think that it's the …' began the man with the ravaged face – but the phrase slithered away unfinished into the mimosas.

Samuel was with us now. He had produced an old musical instrument with strings – or else an old box made into a new musical instrument with strings – and I could see at last why he had been granted chestnut twigs for fingers, for with them he could pick and pluck these strings and draw from them a celestial accompaniment to our vigil, a coloured web of sound surrounding us, pink, pink, celestial pink. Did someone play a flute? And then, quite suddenly, without effort and without warning, I became aware of what it meant. Directly, with a transcendental certainty, the secret of existence had been vouchsafed to me, and it may be that this sudden accession of knowledge gave me an exalted look, surprised anyway, because the others were now staring at me and asking: 'But what has befallen you?'

'There is no problem!' I cried. I had stood up to make my announcement.

'No problem?'

'None. And no need, therefore, to solve it or speak of it or write of it – for now I *know*!'

'What is it that you know? Speak! Speak!'

I was bursting with the knowledge, and only the words for it eluded me.

'Speak! Speak!'

I took in a tremendous breath, drawing in the winds of heaven. 'The world is a ...'

'Yes, yes?'

'... a pink shirt!'

'Yes, yes?'

'Our eyes its buttons!'

'Yes, yes, and then?'

And then I sank down into the mosaic seas, or so I imagine, for I remember nothing more except a wailing watery voice that mingled with the music, possibly Master Jackie's, for the words were English:

'Our eyes its buttons and its buttonholes its buttonholes ...'

* * *

The sun came up as if nothing had happened and caught us trying to harness the tonga-pony – but the tonga-pony did not wish to be harnessed and it seemed unlikely that we could succeed because our reactions and the fumbling of our fingers were still a little other-worldly. Yet finally we did succeed, perhaps because Sikunder recited a charm intended, strictly speaking, for use with camels inhabited by djinns but worth trying with any quadruped you hope to ride or drive:

'Oh God, quiet this unmanageable thing, and remove from me the results of this evil!'

In due course the pony submitted and we clambered into the tonga: and in due course, though slowly and in silence, we reached

Rohri. Outside the waiting-room at Rohri Junction the attendant flew up to me in a state of emotion:

'*Huzoor!*' he cried. '*Huzoor!* Where have you been? There is a terrible man within awaiting you! I tried to make him go, I tried everything, all my wiles, I asked to see his ticket, I ...' – and then, with a little gasp, he saw Sikunder and stopped talking instantly.

Sikunder took no notice of the attendant, however, and had already opened the door of the waiting-room. We could see Kaka sahib sitting tranquilly inside.

'Peace be upon you,' Kaka sahib said as we went in.

'And on you peace,' we replied, formally, and then waited to see what he would say next. He sat looking at us with a very calm face but said nothing. After a few seconds of this silence Sikunder blurted out:

'We have come back to you, Kaka sahib.'

'"We"?'

Sikunder swallowed and said: 'Well, anyway, *I* have.'

Kaka sahib turned to me: 'I see in your eyes, Peter, and also in the eyes of Sikunder, where you have been. Did you think that perhaps *that* would teach you something?'

I stood looking at him, but I did not reply.

'Nothing, then? It taught you nothing?'

I suppose that I was still in part possessed by *bhang*. I said:

'I learnt that ...' I faltered and tried again: 'For a moment I saw that ...' – but looking at the world through the fly-screen doors of the waiting-room, at the water-blue sky and the wispy clouds of winter, at the shining golden air thrown like a veil across the valley of the Indus, I could see that the moment had passed. I said:

'Alas, Kaka sahib, I seem incapable of learning anything.'

About the Author

PETER MAYNE (1908-79) was an English travel writer, revered in particular for his two books on Pakistan and one on Morocco. Peter wrote with a rare, incisive wit and a perfect memory for dialogue and for silences. He was untouched by both the racism of his age and the prejudices of his class, a refreshing example of empathy and humanity who could not resist bubbling over into humour.

Peter was born in Wiltshire, but first travelled out to India aged two. His father was an exotic sort of schoolmaster who specialised in the sons of the ruling princes of India, both as principal of Rajmukar College for twenty years and also as tutor to the Maharajah of Jaipur. After Peter had finished his own schooling in England, he went to Bombay and worked for a firm of ship merchants but was informed that 'he would never make a successful businessman'. Fuelled by his own fluency with languages and vivacity, and his father's easy access into Indian society, he nevertheless had a brilliant social life.

From 1941, Peter served as an RAF liaison officer with the Pathan tribes of the North West Frontier. After the British forces evacuated after Partition in 1947, he witnessed the sectarian violence in Kashmir. He went on to serve the government of Pakistan as Deputy Secretary to the Ministry of Refugees and Rehabilitation. After the tension of Partition had eased, he resigned and travelled slowly westwards. Leaving Spain in 1950, he settled in the back streets of Marrakech to write. All his novels from this period were destroyed. His niece remembers quite a bonfire of typescripts in her parents' English garden one afternoon, including a novel entitled *Wind under the Heart*. But she also recollects a play of his being briefly staged in the West End.

Saints of Sind

By 1953 Peter was back in Pakistan, though fortunately his journal from the Moroccan period found its way to the offices of John Murray who published *The Alleys of Marrakech* in 1954. This was followed by *The Narrow Smile: A Journey back to the North-west Frontier* in 1955 and *Saints of Sind* in 1956. During this halcyon period, Mayne was praised by writers such as Harold Nicolson and Paul Bowles in review after review. All these titles were later revived by Eland as travel classics.

The Private Sea, set on the island of Poros in the Aegean, was published in 1958. Simon Raven wrote, 'This book is a wry piece of work, quiet and funny, light-hearted but yet rather sad. Everyone in the story behaves with consistent shabbiness throughout, but none of them is lacking, for a single instant, in dignity, courtesy or charm.'

In the late '60s Peter Mayne acquired a flat in Athens, which served as a postal address, but he was always a traveller. From 1955–61 he was mostly in Greece, between 1962–64 largely in Istanbul, followed by visits to Cairo between 1966–71. He wrote about Istanbul for the Cities of the World series (published in 1967) and published his last work in 1975: *Friends in High Places: a Season in the Himalayas*. The 'friends' in question were from his youthful years in Bombay. Jagut and Mussoorie were the sons of the exiled Rana Maharajah, who had been Prime Minister of Nepal, and Mayne's account of his visit to the two very different men, one living on an estate by the River Jumna in India, the other in Kathmandu, is interspersed with his research into the 1846 Kot massacre, which changed the course of Himalayan history.

Peter Mayne was one of four children. He was especially close to his younger brother, Jonathan, who was Deputy Keeper of Paintings at the V & A. The two of them shared a vivacious group of friends which included Cyril Connolly, Brian Gysin, Francis Bacon, Osbert Lancaster, Oliver Messel and Ronald Searle.

ELAND

61 Exmouth Market, London EC1R 4QL
Email: info@travelbooks.co.uk

Eland was started forty years ago to revive great travel books that had fallen out of print. Although the list soon diversified into biography and fiction, all the books are chosen for their interest in spirit of place. One of our readers explained that for him reading an Eland is like listening to an experienced anthropologist at the bar – she's let her hair down and is telling all the stories that were just too good to go into the textbook.

Eland books are for travellers, and for readers who are content to travel in their own minds. They open out our understanding of other cultures, interpret the unknown and reveal different environments, as well as celebrating the humour and occasional horrors of travel. We take immense trouble to select only the most readable books and therefore many readers collect the entire, hundred-and-sixty-volume series.

You will find a very brief description of some of our books on the following pages. Extracts from each and every one of them can be read on our website, at www.travelbooks.co.uk. If you would like a free copy of our catalogue, email us
or send a postcard.

ELAND

Libyan Sands
RALPH BAGNOLD
An heroic account of an infatuation with the Model T Ford and the Sahara

An Innocent Anthropologist
NIGEL BARLEY
An honest, funny, affectionate and compulsively irreverent account of fieldwork in West Africa

Memoirs of a Bengal Civilian
JOHN BEAMES
Sketches of 19th-century India painted with the richness of Dickens

Jigsaw
SYBILLE BEDFORD
An intensely remembered autobiographical novel about an inter-war childhood

A Visit to Don Otavio
SYBILLE BEDFORD
The hell of travel and the Eden of arrival in post-war Mexico

Journey into the Mind's Eye
LESLEY BLANCH
An obsessive love affair with Russia and one particular Russian

Japanese Chronicles
NICOLAS BOUVIER
Three decades of intimate experiences throughout Japan

The Way of the World
NICOLAS BOUVIER
A 1950s road trip to Afghanistan, by a legendary young sage

The Devil Drives
FAWN BRODIE
Biography of Sir Richard Burton, explorer, linguist and pornographer

Travels into Bokhara
ALEXANDER BURNES
Nineteenth-century espionage in Central Asia

Turkish Letters
OGIER DE BUSBECQ
Eyewitness history at its best: Istanbul during the reign of Suleyman the Magnificent

An Ottoman Traveller
EVLIYA ÇELEBI
Travels in the Ottoman Empire, by the Pepys of 17th-century Turkey

Two Middle-Aged Ladies in Andalusia
PENELOPE CHETWODE
An infectious, personal account of a fascination with horses, God and Spain

My Early Life
WINSTON CHURCHILL
From North West Frontier to Boer War by the age of twenty-five

A Square of Sky
JANINA DAVID
A Jewish childhood in the Warsaw ghetto and hiding from the Nazis

Chantemesle
ROBIN FEDDEN
A lyrical evocation of childhood in Normandy

Viva Mexico!
CHARLES FLANDRAU
Five years in turn-of-the-century Mexico, described by an enchanted Yankee

Travels with Myself and Another
MARTHA GELLHORN
Five journeys from hell by a great war correspondent

The Trouble I've Seen
MARTHA GELLHORN
Four stories of the Great Depression, offering profound insight into the suffering of poverty

The Weather in Africa
MARTHA GELLHORN
Three novellas set amongst the white settlers of East Africa

The Last Leopard
DAVID GILMOUR
The biography of Giuseppe di Lampedusa, author of The Leopard

Walled Gardens
ANNABEL GOFF
A portrait of the Anglo-Irish: sad, absurd and funny

Africa Dances
GEOFFREY GORER
The magic of indigenous culture and the banality of colonisation

Cinema Eden
JUAN GOYTISOLO
Essays from the Muslim Mediterranean

Goodbye Buenos Aires
ANDREW GRAHAM-YOOLL
A portrait of an errant father, and of the British in Argentina

A State of Fear
ANDREW GRAHAM-YOOLL
A journalist witnesses Argentina's nightmare in the 1970s

A Pattern of Islands
ARTHUR GRIMBLE
Rip-roaring adventures and a passionate appreciation of life in the Southern Seas

Warriors
GERALD HANLEY
Life and death among the Somalis

Morocco That Was
WALTER HARRIS
All the cruelty, fascination and humour of a pre-modern kingdom: Morocco in the 19th and early 20th century

Far Away and Long Ago
W H HUDSON
A childhood in Argentina, and a hymn to nature

Palestine Papers 1917–22
ED. DOREEN INGRAMS
History caught in the making

Holding On
MERVYN JONES
The story of a London dockland street, and the families who lived there

Mother Land
DMETRI KAKMI
A minutely observed Greek childhood on a Turkish island in the 1960s

Red Moon & High Summer
HERBERT KAUFMANN
A coming-of-age novel following a young singer in his Tuareg homeland

Three Came Home
AGNES KEITH
A mother's ordeal in a Japanese prison camp

Peking Story
DAVID KIDD
The ruin of an ancient Mandarin family under the new communist order

Scum of the Earth
ARTHUR KOESTLER
Koestler's escape from a collapsing France in World War II

The Hill of Kronos
PETER LEVI
A poet's radiant portrait of Greece

A Dragon Apparent
NORMAN LEWIS
Cambodia, Laos and Vietnam on the eve of war

Golden Earth
NORMAN LEWIS
Travels in Burma

The Honoured Society
NORMAN LEWIS
Sicily, her people and the Mafia within

Naples '44
NORMAN LEWIS
Naples, surviving the horrors of war through her talent for life

A View of the World
NORMAN LEWIS
Collected adventures of a lifelong traveller of genius

An Indian Attachment
SARAH LLOYD
Life and the love of a Sikh temple servant in a remote Indian village

A Pike in the Basement
SIMON LOFTUS
Tales of a hungry traveller: from catfish in Mississippi to fried eggs with chapatis in Pakistan

92 Acharnon Street
JOHN LUCAS
A gritty portrait of Greece as the Greeks would recognise it, seen through the eyes of a poet

Among the Faithful
DAHRIS MARTIN
An American woman living in the holy city of Kairouan, Tunisia in the 1920s

Lords of the Atlas
GAVIN MAXWELL
The rise and fall of Morocco's infamous Glaoua family, 1893-1956

A Reed Shaken by the Wind
GAVIN MAXWELL
Travels among the threatened Marsh Arabs of southern Iraq

A Year in Marrakesh
PETER MAYNE
Back-street life and gossip in Morocco in the 1950s

Sultan in Oman
JAN MORRIS
An historic journey through the still-medieval state of Oman in the 1950s

Hopeful Monsters
NICHOLAS MOSLEY
A passionate love story at the birth of the atomic age

Full Tilt
DERVLA MURPHY
A lone woman bicycles from Ireland to India in 1963

Tibetan Foothold
DERVLA MURPHY
Six months with recent exiles from Tibet in Northern India

The Waiting Land
DERVLA MURPHY
The spell of the ancient civilisation of Nepal

Where the Indus is Young
DERVLA MURPHY
A mother and her six-year-old daughter explore a wintry Baltistan

In Ethiopia with a Mule
DERVLA MURPHY
By mule across the mountains of Abyssinia

Wheels within Wheels
DERVLA MURPHY
The makings of a traveller: a searingly honest autobiography

The Island that Dared
DERVLA MURPHY
Three journeys through the landscape and history of Communist Cuba

The Caravan Moves On
IRFAN ORGA
Life with the nomads of central Turkey

Portrait of a Turkish Family
IRFAN ORGA
The decline of a prosperous Ottoman family in the new Republic

Sweet Waters
HAROLD NICHOLSON
A turn-of-the-century Istanbul thriller

The Undefeated
GEORGE PALOCZI-HORVATH
The confessions of a dedicated, Hungarian communist, tortured by his own regime

Travels into the Interior of Africa
MUNGO PARK
The first – and still the best – European record of west-African exploration

Lighthouse
TONY PARKER
Britain's lighthouse-keepers, in their own words

The People of Providence
TONY PARKER
A London housing estate, its secrets and some of its inhabitants

Begums, Thugs & White Mughals
FANNY PARKES
William Dalrymple edits and introduces a true portrait of early colonial India

The Last Time I Saw Paris
ELLIOT PAUL
One street, its loves and loathings, set against the passionate politics of inter-war Paris

Rites
VICTOR PERERA
A Jewish childhood and a portrait of Guatemala

A Cure for Serpents
THE DUKE OF PIRAJNO
An Italian doctor and his Bedouin patients, Libyan sheikhs and Tuareg mistress in the 1920s

When Miss Emmie was in Russia
HARVEY PITCHER
Six adventurous British governesses, caught up in the Revolution

Nunaga
DUNCAN PRYDE
Ten years among the Eskimos: hunting, fur-trading and heroic dog-treks

Ask Sir James
MICHAELA REID
The life of Sir James Reid, personal physician to Queen Victoria

A Funny Old Quist
EVAN ROGERS
A gamekeeper's passionate evocation of a now-vanished English, rural lifestyle

The Pharaoh's Shadow
ANTHONY SATTIN
In pursuit of Egypt's past, through her teeming, mysterious and enchanting present

Travels on my Elephant
MARK SHAND
Six hundred miles across India on the back of the much-loved Tara

Valse des Fleurs
SACHEVERELL SITWELL
A day in the life of imperial St Petersburg in 1868

Living Poor
MORITZ THOMSEN
A Peace Corps worker's inside story of Ecuador

The Fields Beneath
GILLIAN TINDALL
London revealed through a micro-history of Kentish Town

Hermit of Peking
HUGH TREVOR-ROPER
The hidden life of the scholar and trickster Sir Edmund Backhouse

The Law
ROGER VAILLAND
The harsh game of life played by the southern Italians

Bangkok
ALEC WAUGH
The story of a city, a monarchy and a nation

The Road to Nab End
WILLIAM WOODRUFF
A story of poverty and survival in a Lancashire mill town

The Village in the Jungle
LEONARD WOOLF
A dark novel of villagers struggling to survive in colonial Ceylon

Death's Other Kingdom
GAMEL WOOLSEY
The tragic arrival of civil war in an Andalusian village in 1936

The Ginger Tree
OSWALD WYND
A Scotswoman's love and survival in early twentieth-century Japan

www.ingramcontent.com/pod-product-compliance
Lightning Source LLC
Chambersburg PA
CBHW031427150426
43191CB00006B/424